JACK HOUSE ASKS THE QUESTIONS

SCOTS QUIZ!

THE COLOUR PICTURES ON THE COVERS

The front cover pictures, beginning with top left, feature: Comforts of Industry as painted by George Morland — the rewards for the Scots family who displayed self discipline and worked hard were a happy, contented and full life; The iron helmet mask is dated from late in the first century A.D. — it was discovered at Newstead, Roxburghshire; Edinburgh Castle painted by Nasmyth — the water you can see is the Nor' Loch which was drained to make way for Princes Street Gardens.

Next are the MacDonald boys of Skye, Sir James and Sir Alexander, who were painted around 1750 — although the wearing of Highland dress was outlawed at that time by Parliament the young gentlemen are seen wearing four different patterns of tartan. Centrepiece is a splendid caricature of the famous Scots comedian, Sir Harry Lauder, which was drawn in 1915. His Highland dress, pawky humour and sentimental songs made him a personification of Scotland to many.

The painting of Mary Queen of Scots is based on a miniature made when she was in prison. It was commissioned by her son, James VI and I, some thirty years after Mary's death, to preserve the memory of the unfortunate monarch whose reign over Scotland was an unhappy succession of tragedies and mistakes. It ended with her execution. The scene of Presbyterian Catechising was painted by John Phillip. This was from a time when the question/answer format was adopted for the instruction of religious doctrine. The chessmen featured were located on the island of Lewis 800 years ago and had been carved by Norsemen. The writing genius, Sir Walter Scott, is pictured with his family. He is bracketed with Shakespeare, Cervantes and Chaucer in the history of literature.

The inside front cover is a painting of Hugh Montgomerie, 12th Earl of Eglington, by an unknown artist. The inside back cover features the Penicuik Jewels of Mary Queen of Scots (circa 16th century). The back cover is from a painting by James Drummond and features one of Edinburgh's most famous riots when the Porteous Mob went rampaging through the Grassmarket to try and right an alleged misjustice.

ABOUT THE AUTHOR

Jack House is a well-known Scot and a journalist of fifty-five years' standing. He has had fifty-three books published, still writes for the Glasgow Evening Times and appears on radio and BBC and Scottish Television.

This new updated edition of Scotland for Fun was published by Lang Syne Publishers Ltd., Newtongrange, Midlothian, in 1983, and printed by Waterside Printers at the Old School, Blanefield, Stirlingshire.

The illustrations, published here for the first time, are by John Mackay.

We would like to thank Hutchinson of London, who published the original in 1960, for their co-operation which made this new edition possible.

© Lang Syne Publishers Ltd., Newtongrange, Midlothian 1983.
© Questions/Answers: Jack House 1960 and 1983.
ISBN O 946264 51 1

CONTENTS

INTRODUCTION

I seem to have been connected with quizzes for years and years. Actually, it is 35 years since the "Round Britain Quiz" was tried out as a substitute for the "Transatlantic Quiz". The BBC had run out of dollars after the war and thought a Britain-based quiz might work. Scotland was chosen to provide the guinea pigs against London. The Scottish team was James Fergusson, then a leader writer on the Glasgow Herald, and me. Fortunately it worked and we went on to broadcast it for 25 years.

This led to other quizzes. For several years I set the questions and was the quizmaster for "Clan Clash" on BBC Scotland radio. This was followed by a television contest called "Quiz-burgh", in which various Scottish burghs competed. Then there was an STV programme, "Town versus Gown", in which I was one of the Town team.

So you might call me a confirmed quizzer, for I still supply questions and answers on request. Some of them are included in this book and anyone with a fair knowledge of Scotland should be able to do well in the 50 sections.

But, even if you don't know much about this 'knuckle-end of England', as a dyspeptic Englishman once called it, you should be able to follow the clues that are in many of the questions. And, at the very least, you'll be learning something about a wonderful country.

One word of warning. Authorities sometimes disagree on 'facts' of history, and other subjects. After all, it depends on whether you're Scots or English, what view you take of the Battles of Bannockburn and Flodden. As far as I can tell, the answers to the 500 questions are accurate, and, where authorities have disagreed, I've tried to give both sides. Still, inaccuracies may have slipped in. Will you please let me know if you find any mistakes?

JACK HOUSE

QUESTIONS

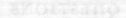

QUIZ NO. 1 # WHAT DO YOU KNOW ABOUT SCOTLAND?

Many people, even including some just across the Border, have peculiar ideas about Scotland. So this first quiz is to test your general knowledge of the country of bens and glens, haggis and heather, Celts and kilts. If you are a Sassenach and can answer half the questions correctly, you should do well in the remaining forty-nine quizzes. If you are Scottish and don't score 75 per cent, you should be ashamed of yourself.

1. The patron saint of Scotland is (a) St. Columba; (b) Robert Burns; (c) St. Andrew; (d) Sir Harry Lauder. Which is correct?

2. The population of Scotland is approximately (a) 500,000; (b) 5,000,000; (c) 15,000,000. Which?

3. Is the national emblem of Scotland (a) the thistle; (b) the Fiery Cross; or (c) the lion rampant?

4. What is the General Assembly?

5. How many counties are there in Scotland? 32

6. The area of Scotland covers—approximately will do again—(a) 10,000 square miles; (b) 30,000 square miles; (c) 50,000 square miles. Which?

7. Which Scottish King became ruler of England as well as of Scotland?

8. What is the farthest distance you can get away from the sea, or salt water, in Scotland: (a) 20 miles; (b) 40 miles; (c) 60 miles; (d) 100 miles?

9. How many mountains are there in Scotland over 4,000 feet?

10. What *is* a Sassenach, anyway?

[11]   *Answers on pages 87–88*

A ben, as most people know, is a mountain in Scotland. It should not be confused with the other Scottish ben, as in 'ben the hoose'. There are some tall tales connected with the bens, but here are ten ben questions which are a matter of fact.

1. What is the Christian name of The Cobbler, and how tall is he?

2. Where is the Duke of Argyll's Bowling Green?

3. From the summit of which murderous mountain is it possible to see 126 other mountains?

4. What big ben is described as 'a vast, bare mass of pink granite surmounted by grey porphyry and agglomerates'?

5. Where will you find the best mountaineering in Great Britain?

6. What is the difference between Ben Tee and Ben Hee? (This is in just for a laugh!)

7. How high are MacLeod's Tables?

8. And how high are Munro's Tables?

9. Where is the greatest area in Britain at an elevation of over 3,000 feet?

10. Which ben is known as 'The Botanist's Paradise'?

QUIZ NO. 3 *DOWN THE GLENS*

One of the most popular Scottish songs is called 'Down in the Glen', and most people know that a glen is the opposite of a ben. A glen is a valley, but, mind you, in Scotland this is a comparative matter. Some glens are valleys between bens, but you've got to climb and climb to get into the valley. However, you should find the going easier in this section than the last.

1. Which is the Glen of Weeping, and why? (Be careful of this one.)

2. Which is the longest glen in Scotland, and how long is it?

3. Which glen is more than 800 feet high and has a piece of grateful granite on its summit (if a glen can have a summit)?

4. On 19th August 1745 a Prince raised his father's flag in a glen. Which Prince and what glen?

5. King Robert the Bruce opened his campaign for the independence of Scotland in 1307—in a glen, of course. Which glen?

6. Which glen gives sanctuary to both rabbits and tigers?

7. In most glens you can become drunk with beauty. But in a particular one you can do even better. Its name goes all over the world. Which is it?

8. In which Scottish glen did Spanish sailors surrender to English soldiers?

9. Three 'literary' glens are Glen Avon, Glen Quharity, and Glen Clunie. Can you mention a famous author associated with each?

10. Thousands visit Scotland's most tragic glen every spring. Can you say why?

See question 8 on page 13 — In which Scottish glen did Spanish sailors surrender to English soldiers?

QUIZ NO. 4 *BONNIE PRINCE CHARLIE*

Scotland has had her share of romantic figures, but to the world at large easily the most romantic Scot is Bonnie Prince Charlie, hero of the '45, various novels, several stage plays, and even film portrayals by such diverse actors as Ivor Novello and David Niven. You'll find Bonnie Prince Charlie cropping up right through this book, but here he has a special section all to himself.

1. Bonnie Prince Charlie is generally known by his first two and his last names, but he had six altogether. What was his full name?

2. Why were his followers called the Jacobites?

3. What significant voyages were made by *La Doutelle* and *L'Heureux*?

4. On 28th August 1745 Bonnie Prince Charlie marched his army over the highest road in Britain. Where is it, and how high is it?

5. How did his wife prevent the Chief of the Clan MacDougall from joining Prince Charles in the '45?

6. What age was Prince Charles when he was defeated by the Duke of Cumberland at the Battle of Culloden? And what age was the Duke?

7. What was Bonnie Prince Charlie's interest in 'Black Friday'?

8. After Culloden, Prince Charles slept in only one real bed. What happened to the sheets from it?

9. More than a quarter of a century later an English literary lion slept in the same bed. Who was he?

10. Though Bonnie Prince Charlie wanted the crown, he was really responsible for 'God Save the King'. Can you tell why?

See question 9 about the English literary lion who slept in the same bed.

Answers on pages 93–94

QUIZ NO. *5* *LOCHS AND LAKES*

If you are English, you may not be able to pronounce 'loch', but you should know something about these pieces of water in Scotland. Many people say 'lock', to the polite amusement of the Scots. But with determination any Sassenach should be able to get that 'ch' sound. Keep trying this exercise: 'It's a braw, bricht, moonlicht nicht on the loch the nicht.' (Translation? 'It's a beautiful, bright, moonlight night on the lake tonight.')

1. Which loch, famous for its bonnie banks, surrounds a foot?

2. And which loch, renowned in history, has eleven islands, is eleven miles round, and has eleven rivers running into it?

3. What loch is far better known as a ben?

4. How many lakes (not lochs) are there in Scotland, and where are they?

5. Where was a loch made into a railway and world-famous gardens?

6. A man-made loch stands in the geographical centre of Scotland. Which is it?

7. How did the Holy Loch in the Firth of Clyde get its name?

8. The Loch of Heaven and the Loch of Hell run into the same piece of water and are separated by a mountain. Where are they?

9. Loch Morar is sometimes called 'the deepest hole in Europe'. Is it approximately (*a*) 1,000 feet deep; (*b*) 2,000 feet; (*c*) 3,000 feet?

10. You've often heard of the Loch Ness monster, but two other lochs have monsters. Just to make it easier for you, they have both been mentioned already in this quiz.

The Loch Ness Monster comes up for air — but which two other Scottish lochs have monsters? See question 10 above.

Answers on pages 95–96

QUIZ NO. 6 *EATING IN SCOTLAND*

Scotland is famous for its food, but some gourmets say the fame rests more in the quality of the raw material than in the local cooking of it. Huge quantities of Scottish beef, Scottish fish (especially salmon and lobsters), and Scottish potatoes go to London for the biggest and best hotels and the West End restaurants. In fact, the 'roast beef of Old England' in these places is invariably Scottish! But what do you know of Scottish dishes in Scotland?

1. How would you make (*a*) Powsowdie; (*b*) How-towdie; (*c*) Cock-a-leekie; (*d*) Partan bree?

2. Where is 'The Land o' Cakes'?

3. What was Mrs. Macnab of Ballater famous for?

4. What's the difference between scone and Scone?

5. Here's the 64,000-dollar question! What is a haggis?

6. If you attend a Burns Supper, you are likely to see accompanying the haggis 'neeps an' champit tatties'. What are they?

7. When do you eat Black Bun, and what's in it anyway?

8. If you're fond of game, which of these birds would you select (for quantity, and not necessarily quality) for dinner—partridge, pheasant or grouse?

9. What foods are these six places famous for: (*a*) Arbroath; (*b*) Dundee; (*c*) Dunlop; (*d*) Forfar; (*e*) Loch Fyne; (*f*) Selkirk?

10. Scotland has a very famous 'grace before meals'. Can you say it, and do you know who is supposed to have composed it?

[19]   *Answers on pages 97–98*

There are two men who could never be kept out of a quiz book on Scotland. One is Bonnie Prince Charlie, subject of Quiz No. 4. The other is Robert Burns, the great Scottish poet, whose 'Immortal Memory' is celebrated all over the world (including Russia and China) on the anniversary of his birth. Here are ten questions about Burns, but you'll find him, like Prince Charles, popping up in other sections throughout this book.

1. Where and when was Robert Burns born?

2. The cottage of his birth, a typical 'but-an'-ben', is preserved to this day. What is peculiar about its position?

3. Which library in which country has the largest collection of books on Burns of any library in the world? And can you say how many different volumes there are?

4. A copy of the first edition of Burns may be worth thousands of pounds. What is its title, and by what name is it generally known?

5. Robert Burns, living in Ayrshire, must have repeatedly seen the mountains of the Isle of Arran, yet he never mentioned them in his works. He did, however, mention Ailsa Craig in a famous song. Can you name the song and say the appropriate lines?

6. The whole world knows and is constantly repeating two famous lines by Burns. They are followed by:

And leave us nought but grief and pain
For promised joy.

What are the two famous lines which precede these?

7. Probably the best-known of all Burns's poems are 'The Cotter's Saturday Night', 'Tam o' Shanter', 'To a Mouse', and 'To a Daisy'. Can you quote the first line of each of these?

8. Scots hate to hear Sassenachs calling their national poet Bobbie Burns. Yet they are wrong in calling him Rabbie. Why?

9. Who was the titled lady who admitted that Burns's conversation carried her off her feet?

10. What is Robert Burns supposed to have said when he was dying?

A titled lady once said that the conversation of Robert Burns carried her off her feet — see question 9.

Robert Burns wrote in Scots (some Scottish writers call it Lallans), but most men of letters in Scotland have written in English. Sir Walter Scott, for example, not only wrote in English but is claimed to be the first modern novelist. And, while a large number of Scottish authors have written about Scotland and the Scots, some have spread their nets wider and have written books of international reputation.

1. Here are four world-famous books: *The Life of Johnson*, *The Wealth of Nations*, *The French Revolution*, and *The Golden Bough*. Who are the Scots who wrote them?

2. Where did Sir James M. Barrie get his ideas for *Peter Pan*?

3. And where is his 'Island that likes to be visited' in the play *Mary Rose*?

4. Who was 'The Man of Feeling'?

5. What are the real names of: (*a*) Hugh McDiarmid; (*b*) Hugh Foulis; (*c*) Saki; (*d*) Christopher North; (*e*) James Bridie?

6. How are George Blake, the novelist, and John Davidson, the poet, linked with James Watt, the inventor, and Captain Kidd, the pirate?

7. Of which great Scottish writer and his wife was it said that it was very good of God to let them marry one another and so make only two people miserable instead of four? And who said it?

8. What towns in Scotland are the 'originals' of Levenford in *Hatter's Castle* by A. J. Cronin;

[22]

Garvel in George Blake's novels; Thrums in J. M.
Barrie's books; and Dundon in *Grey Granite* by
Lewis Grassic Gibbon?

9. Two of the most famous books for children in the
   English language were written by Scots. Can you
   name the titles and authors?

10. Who was the original of Robert Louis Stevenson's
    Dr. Jekyll and Mr. Hyde?

Stevenson's brainwave to create Jekyll and Hyde
— see question 10.

Answers on pages 101–102

Scotland is fortunate in having two sources for her songs—the Highlands and the Lowlands. From the Highlands come the wonderful songs in the Gaelic, known throughout the world in the versions of Mrs. Kennedy Fraser. From the Lowlands come the songs in Lallans, and even in English! Remember, by the way, that the difference between Highlands and Lowlands is not a horizontal line across Scotland. It's a diagonal line, so that places south of Glasgow can be Highland, while Aberdeen in the north is Lowland!

1. Where is 'The Road to the Isles', and who first hiked it?

2. Who was the Scottish crooner who wore a good blue bonnet?

3. You must often have heard 'Jeanie with the light brown hair' and 'I know where I'm going'. What have these two songs in common?

4. There's a Jacobite song which begins:

    The standard on the Braes o' Mar
    Is up and streaming rarely . . .

    It ends:

    Then man to man, and in the van,
    We'll win or die for Chairlie.

    Noble sentiments, but what's wrong with them?

5. A well-known Gaelic song is entitled 'The Tartan of Mary Houston'. How did Mary Houston get her tartan?

[24]

6. A world-famous song has these lines in it:

> We twa hae rin aboot the braes
> An' pu'd the gowans fine . . .

What is the name of the song, and who wrote it?

7. When you sing about the bonnie, bonnie banks of Loch Lomond, you say, 'Ye'll tak' the high road, and I'll tak' the low road.' Why should taking the low road get you to Scotland first?

8. What are a ceilidh, a clarsach, and a coronach?

9. How far do you walk when you're singing a waulking song?

10. What Scottish song of farewell is also an invitation to return?

*A song of farewell that's an invitation to return
— see question 10.*

The spirit of the old Scottish Clans is still kept alive in Scotland, and abroad. When the B.B.C. ran a Scottish quiz on the air, entitled 'Clan Clash', twenty-six different Clan associations entered for the knock-out competition. Many Clans hold regular gatherings, and members come from as far away as America and Australia to attend. There are, by the way, Lowland Clans as well as Highland Clans.

1. Which Clan is proud of its Dutch courage and fights best under the white flag?

2. By what physical feature should you be able to tell a Campbell, and how do you know a Cameron?

3. How could the Farquharsons tell, without counting heads, how many of their Clan had been slain in each battle they fought?

4. Which Clan's slogan is a mountain, and which neighbouring Clan prefers an island?

5. From the sixteenth to the eighteenth century a Clan ran a college on the west shore of Loch Dunvegan, Isle of Skye. Each student took a course lasting seven years. Which Clan was this, and what did they teach?

6. Which anonymous Clan won a battle in Scotland without firing a shot or striking a blow, and where was this battle fought?

7. Which Clan has a Fairy Flag? What are its properties, and where is it kept?

8. The Fiery Cross was sent round the Clan by the Chief to summon them to arms. It's always

portrayed as blazing fiercely. What's wrong with that?

9. Why are the chimes of the Glasgow Tolbooth rung when Cameron of Lochiel visits that city?

10. Who are the Sons of the Seal?

*The chimes ring for Cameron of Lochiel — but why?
See question 9.*

Answers on pages 105–106

There are many clever and witty Gaelic proverbs, but they lose a great deal in translation into English. So I have concentrated here on saws and sayings of the Lowlands of Scotland. My own favourite remark is, 'Whaur's yer Wullie Shakespeare noo?' It's alleged that, on the first night of Home's tragedy, Douglas, in Edinburgh, a galleryite was so thrilled that he shouted this out. But, as an example of overdone patriotic pride, it hardly comes under my heading. Can you say what these sayings mean:

1. He that will to Cupar maun tae Cupar.

2. Keep a calm seugh.

3. Better a wee bush than nae bield.

4. Tak' tent o' time ere time be tint.

5. We'll let that flee stick tae the wa'.

6. Ca' awa' but ca' canny.

7. A stoot he'rt tae a stey brae.

8. Cauld kale het again.

9. It's no' lost what a freen' gets.

10. A causey saint an' a kitchen deil.

QUIZ NO. 12   *MUDDIED OAFS, ETC.*

Some games—notably football and golf—are played all over Scotland. But there are a few truly national sports and I have included these in a later section entitled 'Highland Games'. This particular quiz deals with 'flanneled fools and muddied oafs' and those who are trying to reduce their handicap and their weight. And now that everybody does the Pools, there's no excuse for not knowing the names of Scottish football teams.

1. Here are the nicknames of nine Scottish football teams. The real names opposite are jumbled. You have to put the correct team to each nickname.

   (a) The Doonhamers   Partick Thistle

   (b) The Red Lichties   Motherwell

   (c) The Jags   Arbroath

   (d) The Spiders   Clyde

   (e) The Bairns   Dumbarton

   (f) The Bully Wee   Queen's Park

   (g) The Steel Men   Queen of the South

   (h) The Sons of the Rock   Ayr United

   (i) The Honest Men   Falkirk

2. What would you do if you got into Hell?

3. How many first-class golf courses are there in Scotland: (*a*) 50; (*b*) 150; (*c*) 250?

4. Where is the oldest horse race in the world held?

5. When is there sometimes trouble in Paradise?

6. These Scots were world famous in their own sports. With which sport do you identify: (a) Benny Lynch; (b) K. J. Scotland; (c) Ian Peebles; (d) Ian Black; (e) Eric Liddell; (f) Eric Brown?

7. Where would you go for the Scottish 'Wimbledon'; the Scottish 'Lord's'; the Scottish 'Ascot'; and the Scottish 'Cowes'?

8. Which contest-winning archery group is also the Queen's Bodyguard in Scotland?

9. Which is the oldest Scottish Golf Club? (Be careful of this one!)

10. Here are four drinking vessels. For what sporting event is each awarded: (a) The Calcutta Cup; (b) The Scottish Cup; (c) The Craw's Nest Tassie; (d) The Camanachd Cup?

QUIZ NO. 13   *OUT AND ABOUT*

*Scotland is a wonderful country for the open-air man and woman—
the hiker, the climber, the naturalist, and just the common or
garden walker. The wildest of wild country is never far away—you
can be in the Highlands within half an hour of leaving Glasgow.
Even in towns Scottish children play a game called 'Birds, beasts,
flowers, and fishes', and I invite you to try a version of it now.*

1. The powan and the vendace are found only in
   Scotland. Are they birds, beasts, flowers, or fishes,
   and where do you find them?

2. One of the sights of Scotland is a hedge 80 feet high
   and 600 yards long. What is it made of, and where
   can you see it?

3. If you walked along the beach and into the country,
   you might see a partan, a foumart, a tod, and a
   brock—if you were very lucky. What are they?

4. The last wolf in Scotland was killed in: (a) 1314;
   (b) 1603; (c) 1700. Which of these is correct and
   where did it happen?

5. What and where is the oldest tree in Europe?

6. Which are the three 'worthies of the ocean', according to the Highlanders?

7. Would you rather be a gillie or a garron?

8. Which Scottish island has two animals and a bird
   that are found nowhere else in the world, and what
   are they?

9. Scottish deer forests cover: (a) 25,000 acres; (b)
   250,000 acres; (c) 2,500,000 acres. Which of these
   is correct, and what's odd about a deer forest in
   Scotland?

10. What makes a stag royal?

[31]   *Answers on page* 110

QUIZ NO. 14   *KINGS OF SCOTLAND*

There have been many Kings in Scotland, for at one time the country was divided into small parts and each district had its own King. But I'm not going as far back as that. All the Kings mentioned in this section ruled when Scotland was a complete country. Incidentally, the Kings are given their Scottish numerals here. If I mention James I, I mean James I of Scotland—not the James I of Britain who was James VI of Scotland, if you follow me!

1. What King was known to his devoted subjects as 'Big Head'?

2. What is the connection between a Royal Scottish palace and a building which, though not the Mint, has a lot to do with coppers?

3. Who was the last King of Scotland to speak the Gaelic? And how many other languages did he know?

4. Our Scottish monarchs very often met with a sudden and violent death. Which of them died in these ways: (*a*) By a cannon exploding to bits beside him; (*b*) By being stabbed while escaping from a battle by a man who pretended to be a priest; (*c*) By being murdered by a group of noblemen; (*d*) By falling over a cliff when riding a horse during a storm?

5. Which King was called 'Toom Tabard', and why?

6. A Scottish nobleman, fleeing from a potential enemy, turned his horse's shoes the wrong way round so that possible pursuers would think he was coming instead of going! Later he became King of Scotland. Who was he?

7. One King banned football and golf in Scotland. Another tried to stop his subjects smoking. Who were these spoilsports?

8. Which great Scottish King is buried in two places?

9. What Scottish titles, held in the olden days by royalty in Scotland, are taken by the Prince of Wales?

10. And, just for a change, a question about an English monarch. Which King of England is known to history as 'The Hammer of the Scots'?

Why did the nobleman turn the horseshoes back to front?
A poser in question 6.

Scotland's famous Queen is, of course, Mary Queen of Scots—as much a heroine of plays and films as Bonnie Prince Charlie is a hero. But I hope to show you that we had other Queens in Scotland too. Then we have a special reason for regarding Her Majesty Queen Elizabeth as a Scottish Queen. I can say no more, or I'll be giving away some of the answers before I start asking the questions.

1. Where did Mary Queen of Scots spend her last night on Scottish soil?

2. The oldest building in Edinburgh is named after a Scottish Queen. What is the building and which Queen was she?

3. The first King of Britain was born in Scotland. Who was his mother and where was he born?

4. Her Majesty Queen Elizabeth and the Queen Mother have four Royal homes in Scotland. What are they called and where are they?

5. What residential connection is there between H.R.H. Princess Margaret and Shakespeare's favourite Scottish King, Macbeth?

6. Who was the youngest Queen that Scotland ever had?

7. Shortly before he died, James V of Scotland was told of the birth of a daughter. He is supposed to have said, 'It cam' wi' a lass, and it will gang wi' a lass.' What was 'it' and who were the lasses? Maybe it will help if I tell you that he was right!

[34]

8. When the Royal Scots parade before Royalty, they always march past to 'The Daughter of the Regiment'. Why should this be?

9. Queensferry stands just beside the Forth Bridge. Which Queen gave it that name?

10. Mary Queen of Scots could speak French better than she could speak English or Scots. Where was she born?

A Queensferry name poser — see question 9.

Answers on pages 113–114

THE CAPITAL OF SCOTLAND

Edinburgh is rightfully regarded as one of the most beautiful cities in the world. It is the Capital of Scotland and the home of a great International Festival of the Arts. All tourists have heard of Edinburgh Castle and Princes Street, and perhaps the Royal Mile. But there is more to Edinburgh than that, as I shall now proceed to demonstrate.

1. A 'Geordie', of all people, gave Edinburgh its name. Who was he?

2. Which King made Edinburgh the Capital of Scotland?

3. Edinburgh is sometimes called 'The Modern Athens', and sometimes 'Auld Reekie'. Can you explain these names?

4. One of the main features of Princes Street is the tall monument to Sir Walter Scott. What happened to its architect?

5. Where in Edinburgh will you find 110 imaginary portraits of the Kings of Scotland, and how much are they worth?

6. I mentioned the Royal Mile in my introduction. What, exactly, is the Royal Mile?

7. Another great feature of Princes Street is the Floral Clock. It has a circumference of thirty-eight feet. How many plants does it contain, and when were they first planted?

8. What part did Edinburgh play in Henry the Eighth's 'Rough Wooing'?

9. Arthur's Seat is an extinct volcano right in the middle of the city. Why did it get that name?

10. What is Edinburgh Zoo principally famous for?

Answers on pages 115–116

GLASGOW BELONGS TO ME

Just forty-five miles across country from Edinburgh lies the City of Glasgow, and it's amazing that two towns, so near in one small country, should be so different. Most people have got their idea of Glasgow from Will Fyffe's famous song, 'I Belong to Glasgow', of which there is now even a Russian version. But Glasgow is a lot more than 'Argyle Street on a Saturday night'.

1. Put these five towns in order of size of population—Edinburgh, Birmingham, Glasgow, Liverpool, Dundee.

2. Glasgow has been described as 'a great Victorian city'. But how old are: (*a*) its Cathedral; (*b*) its University; *(c)* its first prison; *(d)* its oldest house?

3. What are: (*a*) The Hielan'man's Umbrella; (*b*) The Barrows; (*c*) The Butts?

4. Which Glasgow football team provided the whole of the Scottish eleven that met England in the first Soccer International? And what was the result of the game?

5. Can you name the Glasgow district which has inspired a novel, a play, a film, and a ballet?

6. In what part of Glasgow would you be reminded of New York?

7. What song about Ireland, written by an Englishman, and heard in the Isle of Man, was made world famous by Glasgow men?

8. Glasgow is famous for its art galleries, and has the world's finest collection of pictures by an overseas

artist who was a very controversial figure. Who was he?

9. What is meant by 'The Glasgow School'?

10. 'Glasgow made the Clyde, and the Clyde made Glasgow.' This is a well-known saying in Scotland. What does it mean?

A question of football in number four.

SERMONS IN STONES—
1. STATUES

Scotland is as full of memorials as any other country, some famous, some important, many local, and a lot that are just funny. But statues and monuments have not been as popular in recent years as they were in Victorian days and earlier. We're more apt to have a memorial in the form of playing fields today. However, here's a first selection of memorials in Scotland, and we're starting with statues.

1. What famous hero of pantomime is commemorated by a statue in Largo, Fife?

2. Why should King William I of Prussia present a statue to Peterhead, and whose statue is it?

3. Where was the first outside statue erected to Sir Walter Scott?

4. What public place in a Scottish town has the largest number of statues to be found in one group in Britain?

5. Who is the man on the top of the lofty column on Lady Hill, Elgin?

6. What memorial to a famous author, facing the place where he was born, is a replica of a statue on the banks of the River Thames?

7. Whose statue seems to be pointing the way to the entrance of a well-known Scottish theatre?

8. Why should there be a statue of Robert Burns's Highland Mary on Castle Hill, Dunoon?

9. There is a statue to a dog in Edinburgh. Why should this dog be so honoured?

10. What is peculiar about the statue of William Ewart Gladstone in George Square, Glasgow?

[39]   *Answers on pages* 119–120

SERMONS IN STONES— 2. MONUMENTS

The way I see it, a monument is not a statue, but it can contain a group of statuary. And a monument need not have a representation of the person or persons it is commemorating. Some monuments are towers or cairns. But, while your mind is on memorials, you should be in just the right mood to tackle this one. Scotland has at least as many monuments as it has statues, but they are more widely spaced.

1. At Taynuilt in the Highlands and Glasgow in the Lowlands, monuments were erected to an English national hero long before any were put up in England. Who was the hero?

2. What long pencil has the figure '1263' on it, and why?

3. Which is the largest monument to one man in Scotland?

4. Where in Scotland is there a memorial which includes white mice, carrier pigeons, and canaries?

5. There is a cairn in Scotland erected to the memory of John Cobb. Where is it, and why is it there?

6. The Well of the Seven Heads tells its story in English, Gaelic, French, and Latin. What is that story and where is the Well?

7. A Scottish island has a tower in memory of a famous soldier of World War One. Who is he, and why is the tower there?

8. In which monument does the sound of a closing door take fifteen seconds to reverberate? Clues? Well,

it took fifteen years to build and cost a Duke £100,000.

9. At three different points on the Firth of Clyde there are monuments or memorials to Henry Bell of Helensburgh. Why?

10. Where is the monument to the Commandos who served in World War Two, and why should it be there?

What and where is the Well of the Seven Heads
— see question 6.

The Scots are every bit as superstitious as anybody else. They hate to spill salt or break a mirror or walk under a ladder. But, besides all these common superstitions, the Scots have some that are peculiarly their own. How many, I wonder, do you know? But I must point out that there are unbelievers in Scotland too. For instance, in Glasgow there is the Thirteen Club, which has thirteen members and always meets when the calendar announces Friday the 13th.

1. Why do travellers on trains passing over the Forth Bridge toss a coin from the window for luck?

2. A man named Sinclair will never cross the Ord of Caithness, the boundary between the counties of Caithness and Sutherland, on a Monday. What are the Sinclairs worried about?

3. Most hearts are held in high esteem, but there's one heart that people are prone to spit on. Where is it?

4. Who will turn back home if, on his way to his work, he meets a minister?

5. What is 'The Curse of Scotland'?

6. What is a 'First Foot', and what colour must he be?

7. Why, in the Highlands, do they sometimes put a horseshoe in an infant's cradle?

8. And what, in the Lowlands, do you do with a 'christening piece'?

9. If a Scotsman's horse turns widdershins, he turns pale. What is widdershins, and why is he worried?

10. Where do people tie a piece of rag to a tree and make a wish, and where do they knock a penny into a tree with the same idea?

QUIZ NO. 21 *WHICH SCOT SAID THIS?*

There are some phrases that everyone uses at one time or another, and there are some quotations that spring readily to our lips. Here are ten quotations, some well known, others that you really ought to know. The point is that every one of them was made originally by a Scot. Can you identify the author of each quotation?

1. 'Britons never, never, never will be slaves!'

2. 'Coming events cast their shadows before.'

3. 'O wad some Power the giftie gie us to see oursels as ithers see us!'

4. 'No one knows a country till he has walked through it; he then tastes the sweets and the bitters of it.'

5. 'I do indeed come from Scotland, but I cannot help it.'

6. 'From their smoky beehives, ten stories high, the unwashed look down upon the open squares and gardens of the wealthy.'

7. 'We fight not for glory nor for wealth nor honour, but for that freedom which no good man surrenders but with his life.'

8. 'That nightmare of gulf and eminence, of gash, and peaks afloat upon the swirling mists . . . haunted for ever with wailing airs and rumours, ghosts calling in the deeps of dusk and melancholy, legends of horror and remorse.'

9. 'They have said. What say they? Let them say.'

10. 'Charm is a kind of bloom on a woman. If you have it, you don't need to have anything else. If you don't have it, it doesn't matter what else you have.'

[43]   *Answers on page* 125

THE RIVERS OF SCOTLAND

The rivers of Scotland are not very long by the standards of the Danube, the Volga or the Mississippi, but they have as much variety, beautiful scenery and fine fishing as any rivers in the world —and more than most. There are no finer salmon anywhere than those which fight their way up Scottish rivers to the place where they were spawned. In any case, Scottish rivers are long enough to keep you busy with these questions.

1. Which river is famous for salmon, ships, and sugar?

2. Another river famous for salmon (and for whisky) is the fastest in Scotland. Which is it?

3. Here are six well-known Scottish rivers: Clyde, Dee, Forth, Spey, Tweed, Tay. Can you put them in order according to length?

4. Two Scottish rivers, the Clyde and the Glass, start with quite different names. What are their original names?

5. You'd swear that the Rivers Murray, Murchison, Lachlan, Mackenzie, Fraser, and Hamilton were in Scotland, but they're not. Can you say in which countries you'll find them?

6. Over which river in Scotland was a bridge built out of spite?

7. What did the Duchess of Hamilton, the Duchess of Montrose, the Marchioness of Lorne and the Countess of Breadalbane have to do with a Scottish river?

8. Each big town of Scotland is built on a river—with one exception. It's built on two rivers. Which town is it, and what are the names of the rivers?

9. Here are some smaller towns built on rivers. Can you put the right river against each town?

(a) Pitlochry   .   .   Dee

(b) Brechin .   .   .   Forth

(c) Dumfries   .   .   Garry

(d) Balmoral   .   .   Nith

(e) Kelso   .   .   .   South Esk

(f) Hawick .   .   .   Tweed

(g) Stirling .   .   .   Teviot

10. Only one river in Scotland has passenger tunnels beneath it. Which is it?

Fastest river in Scotland? See question 2.

[45]   *Answers on page 126*

QUIZ NO. 23 CLOTHES MAKE THE SCOTSMAN (AND SCOTSWOMAN)

Outside her own country, Scotland is more famous for tartan than any other phase of fashion—so much so, that tartans are now manufactured in Europe, America, and even Asia. Well, we can't have a quiz about clothes in Scotland without bringing in tartan. But I hope to show you (if you don't know already) that Scotland has some other claims to fashionable fame, even though the fashions may be those of a bygone day.

1. What famous article of Scottish clothing was brought to Scotland by shipwrecked Spanish sailors?

2. How many yards of tartan are there in a kilt?

3. How did tweed cloth get its name?

4. Why do some Scottish Clans have a hunting tartan as well as an everyday tartan? And how does a dress tartan differ from these?

5. Where would you wear a philabeg?

6. What connection has linen with high finance in Scotland?

7. Kilmarnock, Balmoral, and Glengarry are three parts of Scotland which have their own version of an article of clothing. What is it?

8. Spats are not much worn in Scotland now, except by kilted regiments. What makes the spats worn by the Gordon Highlanders unique?

9. The Sheik of Araby and his friends always bought their head-dresses in Scotland. Can you say where?

10. A Scot gave his name to an article of clothing which is worn universally. Who was he?

[46]   *Answers on pages 127–128*

Scotland has as many castles to the square mile as anywhere else in the world. Most of them, unfortunately, are in ruins. The Vikings and the English (notably under Edward I) kept 'dinging them doon', and what were left became buildings that 'Oliver Cromwell knocked abaht a bit', as the song has it. Even as ruins, however, there are some very fine castles, and some very fine tales to go along with them.

1. Sir Walter Scott wrote about Castle Dangerous and Tillietudlem Castle. Which castles were the 'originals' of these?

2. What connection has Culzean Castle in Ayrshire with the White House in Washington, U.S.A.?

3. What is the geographical difference between Castle Gloom and Doom Castle?

4. Which Scottish castle, often in the news, was 'my dearest Albert's own creation'?

5. In which castle was kept the Stone of Destiny, used in the coronation ceremony of the Scottish Kings?

6. Of which castle did Shakespeare write:

    This castle hath a pleasant seat. The air nimbly and sweetly recommends itself unto our gentle senses.

7. What Scottish castle was used as the headquarters of a money-making scheme by a Danish Princess?

8. To which Scottish nobles do these castles belong: *(a)* Floors Castle; *(b)* Glamis Castle; *(c)* Inveraray Castle?

[47]

9. Which castle has an esplanade where executions have been replaced by entertainment?

10. Which Scottish castle did Queen Victoria think looked like a factory?

Queen Victoria was not amused — see question 10.

You may wonder why I have headed this section 'Scotch Drink' instead of 'Scottish Drink'. Well, it happens to be the title of a poem by Robert Burns, and I couldn't do better than follow the Immortal Bard. Also, we never talk about the wine of our country as Scottish whisky. It's always Scotch—a description it shares with haggis, shortbread, broth, terriers and comedians. But there are other drinks in Scotland, as you see here.

1. What is a deoch an doruis? If you heard Harry Lauder, it sounded like 'a wee doch an' doris'.

2. In big cities children used to make (and still do in some places) sugarolly water. What on earth is that?

3. Atholl Brose is carried into the Sergeants' Mess of the Argyll and Sutherland Highlanders every Hogmanay, and a quaich given to every officer and N.C.O. What is Atholl Brose?

4. And, while we're about it, what is a quaich?

5. Why would most people prefer a Scots pint of ale to an English pint?

6. Why, in the eighteenth century, was claret the favourite wine of Scotland while port was the favourite wine of England?

7. What is the most important ingredient in Scotch whisky?

8. If you sing 'Auld Lang Syne' properly, you sing about 'a richt guid willie waught'. What is a richt guid willie waucht?

[49]

9. What drink is made from a recipe said to have been given to a Highland Clansman by Bonnie Prince Charlie?

10. Every night of the week tankers full of a certain liquid go by road to London. What is this precious liquid which Glasgow has and London hasn't?

A secret recipe for Bonnie Prince Charlie — see question 9.

MISTY ISLANDS OF THE HIGHLANDS (AND LOWLANDS)

Scotland has an immense number of islands surrounding her shores. The Hebrides alone number more than 500. The islands I have mentioned in this section are all islands that you might reasonably be expected to know. If there are any you don't, then you should arrange to visit them as soon as possible. The Scottish islands are wonderful for holidays.

1. What Scottish counties are entirely composed of islands?

2. On which island will you find Fingal's Cave?

3. Duncan and Macbeth are buried on the same island. It is sometimes known as the Cradle of Scottish Christianity. What is its name?

4. Why should you be careful if you are sailing near the Island of Canna?

5. What very famous group of Scottish islands is said to have existed 'since before the Himalayas were beneath the seas'?

6. The Black Isle and Isle of Whithorn are almost at opposite ends of Scotland. What have they in common?

7. Great Britain annexed an island off the Atlantic coast in 1955, and made sure it was still British in 1959. Which island?

8. What Scottish island was taken by the Spaniards when they planned an attack on Britain?

9. Which is the most musical island in Scotland?

10. What Scottish island was used as a prison for English captives, Covenanters, and Jacobites—not all at once, of course!

Answers on page 132

QUIZ NO. **27** GHAISTIES AN' GHOULIES AN' LANG LEGGIT BEASTIES

To which I should add 'And Things that go bump in the night'!
Scotland has its ghosts, its wizards and witches, its fairies and its
monsters. I mean human monsters—or maybe half-human is the
right description—and not something that is quite real, like the
Loch Ness Monster. I hope you get the answers to this quiz right,
but you are at liberty to doubt your results.

1. Which Scottish castle has a secret chamber, and who (or what) is kept inside?

2. Mount Everest has its Abominable Snowman, but there is a mountain in Scotland with a Great Grey Man. Which mountain is it?

3. Where would you be likely to meet a kelpie? And what *is* a kelpie?

4. Has anyone ever died from 'the dead man's bite'?

5. In only one place in Scotland will you find supernatural beings called Bocans and Bleaters. Where is it, and how can you tell a Bocan from a Bleater?

6. Why would you hate to hear a banshee wail?

7. The Trows love music and dancing, so what is their connection with a Norwegian composer whose family came from Scotland? And what are Trows?

8. Where is Granny Kempock, and what special powers does she possess?

9. In which Scottish castle might you meet a ghost on the Bluidy Stair?

10. On what night of the year are witches, evil spirits, warlocks, and the like most active?

QUIZ NO. 28 *IS THIS A RECORD?*

I have been a journalist for more than fifty years, and I know that one of the most dangerous statements that can be made in print is, 'This is a record'. As sure as you announce a record, somebody comes along and beats it. So that is why this quiz is headed by a question. As far as I know, the records mentioned here are records. If you can beat any of them, please write and tell me.

1. Where were the first skyscrapers built? (Not counting the Tower of Babel, of course!)

2. Where was the biggest vine in the world?

3. Where are the loftiest cliffs in the British Isles?

4. Where is the steepest road in Britain?

5. Where is the highest waterfall in Britain?

6. Where was the first cast-iron building erected in the world?

7. Where is the highest main-line railway in Britain?

8. Where is the largest football stadium in Europe (including Russia)?

9. Where (and when) was the first medical school in Britain founded?

10. Where were the world's biggest passenger liners built?

Just as the Scots still talk about 'The Auld Alliance' with France, they still call England 'The Auld Enemy'. But this is not meant to be taken seriously. It's most often applied when football internationals come along, because to the Scots the international match with England (especially if it's held in Scotland) is the highlight of the football year.

1. Which outspoken Englishman said, 'Oatmeal is a food given to horses in England, and to men in Scotland.' (And what was the Scottish reply?)

2. Which English author described what as 'The most beautiful and moving of the recent works of man'?

3. English poets have often written on Scottish subjects. Can you place the proper poem opposite each author's name in this list?

(*a*) Lord Byron . . 'Yarrow Revisited'

(*b*) Gerard Manley Hopkins 'Epitaph on a Jacobite'

(*c*) John Keats . . 'Flannan Isle'

(*d*) Wilfrid Wilson
    Gibson . . . 'Inversnaid'

(*e*) Thomas Babbington
    Macaulay . . 'Sonnet written upon the
                    top of Ben Nevis'

(*f*) Robert Southey . 'The Burial of Sir John
                    Moore after Corunna'

(*g*) Charles Wolfe . . 'The Inchcape Rock'

(*h*) William Wordsworth 'English Bards and Scotch
                    Reviewers'

4. Who described which Scottish town as 'The beautifullest little city I have seen in Britain. . . . The four principal streets are the fairest for breadth and the finest built that I have ever seen in one city together.' And when?

5. And who described which Scottish town as 'The Cancer of Empire'. And when?

6. Who wrote in his *Journal*, after he had visited Edinburgh: 'How long shall the capital city of Scotland and the chief street of it stink worse than a common sewer'?

7. An Englishman translated this description of the Scots warriors by a Frenchman: 'These Scottishmen are right hardy and sore travailling in harness and in wars, for when they will enter into England, within a day and a night they will drive their whole host twenty-four mile.' Who wrote this, and who was the translator, and what was the period?

8. What great English writer asked: 'Stands Scotland where she did?'

9. What very famous song asks that the 'knavish tricks' of the Scots against England be frustrated?

10. Who said and when: 'I can stand at the Mercat Cross of Edinburgh, and within an hour I can shake by the hand fifty men of genius'?

THE SAINTS GO MARCHING IN

Scotland has Saints of her own, and also shares a large number of Saints with other countries. Since Scotland is predominantly Protestant, most of our Saints are decidedly historical. Whatever your religion, you should be interested in the saintly men and women of the past, especially those who played a big part in the making of Scotland.

1. Which Queen of Scotland was also a Saint?

2. The Patron Saint of a Scottish city has two names. What are they and which city is it?

3. The first stone church in Scotland was built by a Saint. Which Saint and where is it?

4. The flag of Scotland is also the symbol of a Saint. Which Saint, and where was he once commemorated on another flag?

5. A senior Scottish football team is known as 'the Saints', and their followers sing 'When the Saints go marching in' as their anthem. What is the team's name and why did they choose it?

6. Two Scottish Saints raced for an island, and one of them won the race by sleight of hand. Who were they and what was the trick?

7. Why were men who drank out of the cup of St. Magnus watched carefully?

8. What Scottish monastery, built by a Saint, stood for 1,000 years?

[56]

9. What Scottish town which bears the name of a Saint was founded by another Saint altogether?

10. The old name of Perth indicated which Saint was the city's patron. What was the former name of the city, and the name of the Saint?

Those who drank from this cup were watched carefully — why? See question 7.

Answers on page 137

THE DEVIL A SAINT WOULD BE

To be fair, we can't have a quiz on the Saints without having one on the Devil too. His Satanic Majesty has a peculiar hold on Scottish hearts. It's not too much to say that the Deil is quite popular in Scotland. He is a favourite character in fiction and on the stage. And the very fact that he is known in Scotland as the Deil shows that the Scots feel they have a proprietary right in him.

1. Who is (a) Auld Hornie; (b) Auld Clootie; (c) Auld Nick?

2. Where is the Devil's Mill, and why is it like the Deil's Cauldron?

3. Robert Burns was fond of the Deil. Can you name three of his works which either deal with the Deil or bring him in as an important character?

4. James Bridie was just as fond of the Deil as Robert Burns was. Can you name three plays by Bridie which have the Deil featuring prominently in them?

5. What is 'The Bad Fire'?

6. How did the Devil's Beef-Tub gets its name, and where is it?

7. What musical instrument can the Deil play?

8. Why should you be very careful of the Devil's Elbow?

9. What is the difference between Devil's Point and Devil's Dyke?

10. What does a Scot mean when he says: 'Deil tak' the hinmost'?

 Answers on pages 138–139

Everyone knows the songs of Scotland, especially the wonderful collection by Robert Burns. Scotland has its music too, and particularly the great music of the bagpipes. There are more people playing and listening to the pipes in Scotland today than at any time in our history. There are other kinds of music—symphonies, concertos, Scottish country dances, and even jazz—in Scotland. And Scotland has inspired some of the greatest of composers.

1. What popular air for the pipes was written originally by a well-known composer for an equally well-known opera?

2. Which European composer was inspired by Fingal's Cave and wrote a piece of music about it?

3. When the song 'The Road to the Isles' is played as a pipe tune, what is its title?

4. Which musical instrument has been banned as a weapon of war?

5. For what types of music are these Scots famous: *(a)* Alexander Gibson; *(b)* Jimmy Shand; *(c)* Iain Hamilton; *(d)* Rod Stewart?

6. What sort of music would you expect to hear if you were at a concert where puirt-a-beul was announced? ('Highland music' is *not* a satisfactory answer!)

7. Who wrote 'The Scotch Symphony'?

8. What is the difference between Pibroch and Piob Mhor?

9. Who was the Scot who played, in 1945, 'the finest music in the world'?

10. What famous Italian opera has a Scottish story?

Away back in Quiz No. 12 I promised you a section on Highland Games, as opposed to Lowland sport. Now I'm asking questions both about the kind of games that are peculiar to the Highlands (though they are also played in the Lowlands—by Highlanders in exile, of course), and about the Highland Games, or sports gatherings, which start in the summer and go on into the autumn.

1. At what Highland Games is there the March of the Thousand Pipers?

2. There are eleven men in a Soccer team, fifteen men in a Rugger team. How many men are in a shinty team?

3. What is the trunk of a tree used for at the Highland Games?

4. An ancient Scottish game is usually played outdoors in the Highlands and indoors in the Lowlands. What is it?

5. One regular athletic event in the Highland Games is not represented by any similar event in the Olympic Games. There are similarities in the Olympic Games to such Highland events as putting the stone and throwing the hammer. But what is this odd man out?

6. What is said to be the fastest ball game in the world —so fast that spectators hardly see the ball at all?

7. When and where are the Royal Highland Games held?

8. In what game is a clean sweep even more important than usual?

[60]

9. At which Highland Gathering are girl dancers not allowed to wear the kilt?

10. If somebody gave you a caman, would you use it at a bonspiel?

Fastest ball game in the world? See question 6.

   Answers on page 142

We've dealt with bens, glens, lochs, rivers, and islands so far, and now here is a quiz about the general geography of Scotland. Scotland isn't so very large, but there's a great deal of variety in the land. There is even a great deal of variety in the climate—though you maybe wouldn't think that from these B.B.C. weather bulletins!

1. What is the difference between the Carse and the Merse?

2. Where is Scotland's earthquake centre?

3. Which is the county town of Berwickshire? (Don't rush this one.)

4. There's no water in this quiz, so can you say where three dry lochs are?

5. Fingal's Cave is on an island, but where is Fingal's Grave?

6. What village, where gold was once mined, is the highest in Scotland?

7. Robert Burns described the length of Scotland as 'frae Maidenkirk to Johnny Groats'. What are the proper names of these two places, and what is the distance between them?

8. What is the most northerly point on the mainland of Scotland, and what is its approximate distance from Land's End? (Again, don't rush!)

9. What southern land in the north is the most thinly populated county in Britain.

10. You know how often Scottish place-names start with the same prefix: Auchtermuchty, Auchterarder, Kilmarnock, Kilbirnie, and so on. Here are some prefixes. Can you put the correct meaning opposite each?

(a) Auch . . Height

(b) Ard . . . Upper, high-lying

(c) Balloch . . Cell or church

(d) Beg . . . Fort

(e) Buie (a suffix) . Stone

(f) Cam . . Yellow

(g) Clach . . Little

(h) Dhu or Dubh . A pass

(i) Dun . . . A rock

(j) Kil . . . Field

(k) Ochter or Auchter Crooked

(l) Craig . . Black

QUIZ NO. 35 *ALL AT SEA*

More Scottish geography, but this quiz deals with the sea as well as the land, and particularly those pieces of Scotland which come in touch with the sea. If you've been working steadily through this book, you'll know that no part of Scotland is more than thirty-nine miles from salt water. I hope it's unnecessary to explain to you that a 'Firth' is a river estuary, or should I have made that my first question?

1. In what way does the Pentland Firth differ from the Firth of Clyde, the Firth of Forth and the Cromarty Firth?

2. One of the beauty spots of Scotland is the region called the Kyles of Bute. What is a Kyle?

3. The last sea-going paddle steamer in the world still sails round the coasts of Britain. What is her name and where does she come from?

4. How many Capes are there in Scotland, and where are they?

5. The Firth of Clyde is famed for its islands, but how many islands can you name in the Firth of Forth?

6. Which of these is the most important island in the Firth of Forth and why?

7. Where will you find bridges which actually cross the Atlantic?

8. The most northerly habitation in Britain is by the sea. What is it?

9. How many firths are there completely within the borders of Scotland?

10. Why do most people avoid the Strait of Corrievreckan?

[64]   *Answers on page 145*

QUIZ NO. 36   *FIGHTING MEN*

Scotland is famous for its fighting men, both Highland and Lowland. In one war after another Scotland has contributed far more men than its size would warrant. The outstanding example was in the first half of the nineteenth century, when the Isle of Skye alone raised 10,000 soldiers to fight for Britain. Of that 10,000 no fewer than twenty-one became generals.

1. In the old days fighting Highlanders had no such thing as steel helmets. What was their substitute?

2. What regiment well known to Londoners was raised in a Scottish Border town?

3. There is only one 'private army' allowed in Britain. Where are its headquarters, and who's in charge?

4. Which Scottish regiment takes its rifles into church during the service and posts guards round the church? And why?

5. How did the oldest Highland regiment get its name?

6. Which famous old Scottish football club was started by soldiers?

7. The senior infantry regiment of the British Army started by fighting for Sweden. How did this come about?

8. What happened when the Earl o' Mar's Greybreeks mingled with the Glesca Keelies?

9. And, while we're on odd names, who are Pontius Pilate's Bodyguard?

10. Who are second to none, who are fearless, and who are waiting?

QUIZ NO. 37 *THE ROOT OF ALL EVIL*

The Scots are alleged to have an inordinate fondness for money. Everybody has heard of the 'canny Scot', and he is supposed to be typified by the Aberdonian—in actual fact, one of the most generous of men. Some people think that Harry Lauder gave the world the idea of the mean, over-thrifty Scotsman, but this reputation was known throughout Europe long before that.

1. If you want to make money in Scotland, you should search for the Jacobites' treasure. Where is it hidden?

2. How many different kinds of pound notes are in current use in Scotland?

3. Where did the Scottish 'gold rush' take place?

4. And where is gold regularly extracted from the air in Scotland?

5. In what bay has the Duke of Argyll a financial interest?

6. What Scots turned down an offer of £30,000, and why?

7. Which would you rather have—a plack, a merk, a doit, or a bodle?

8. Who was the Scot who gave away £12,000,000 in Britain and 288,000,000 dollars in the U.S.A., and where was he born?

9. What does the Bank of England owe to Scotland?

10. Where did Robert Burns write these lines (the last two of twelve):

    > For lack o' thee, I leave this much-loved shore,
    > Never, perhaps, to greet auld Scotland more!

    And what is 'thee'?

*Nothing could be less true than the oft-repeated statement that the
Scots take their pleasures sadly. The Scots celebrate so vigorously
that they are inclined to make even a funeral a sort of celebration.
There are big national festivities, and all over the country there
are strongly supported local festivities. Exiles come from the far
corners of the earth to see them again.*

1. What happens when they Burn the Clavie at
   Burghead, and when do they do it?

2. There is one happy phrase you must not repeat on
   Hogmanay. What is it, and why shouldn't you
   say it?

3. Where and when do Scots set a Viking galley
   alight?

4. When would you hope to see a procession of
   disguised people carrying turnip lanterns?

5. The 'Uppies' play the 'Doonies' in a Scottish town
   every Candlemas. Who are they, which town
   is it, and when is Candlemas?

6. Where will you find the Burry Man, and how often
   does he appear?

7. Where would you go to see the coronation of:
   (*a*) The Lanimer Queen; (*b*) The Marymass
   Queen; (*c*) The Queen of the South?

8. Who carries a lump of coal about with him on
   December 31st?

9. At one Scottish University an annual pageant is held in which the main character is a girl, played by a male student. Who is the girl and where is the University?

10. What is 'Whuppity Scoorie'?

University Pageant — but where? See question 9.

By this time you must realize that Scotland has at least two heroes—
Bonnie Prince Charlie and Robert Burns! But in this list of ten
questions I promise you that neither Bonnie Prince Charlie nor
Robert Burns is mentioned even once. And, by the way, will you
please remember that a hero to one nation may be a villain to
another?

1. A Glasgow magistrate is one of the heroes (I consider
   the principal one) of a novel by Sir Walter Scott.
   Where is there a tree with a somewhat uncon-
   ventional memorial to him?

2. What educational boast could be made by the Lord
   of the Isles who challenged the King of Scots at the
   Battle of Harlaw in 1411?

3. The hero of the Relief of Lucknow was known as
   Lord Clyde. What was his real name?

4. What hero experimented on himself before giving
   the world a great medical boon?

5. An American hero, who gave his name to a dance,
   was really a Scot, but not considered a hero in
   Scotland. Who was he, and why should the Scots
   dislike him?

6. Which regiment formed the immortal 'Thin Red
   Line' at Balaclava?

7. A great Scottish hero lost his life in trying to save
   another hero's heart. Who was he, and whose was
   the heart?

8. Who was the Field Marshal of Sweden who was
   regarded as a hero by the Scottish Covenanters?

9. What did Hal o' the Wynd do that made him a hero in Perth?

10.

Not a sound was heard, not a funeral note,
As his corpse to the ramparts we hurried . . .

These are the opening lines of a poem to a 'hero we buried'. Who was he?

Magistrate was Scott's hero — see question 1.

Oh, yes, we have our heroines too in Scotland. I promise you that Mary Queen of Scots is not included in this section, but I can't repeat the promise I made in the last quiz about Bonnie Prince Charlie! On the other hand, I must repeat the warning I have already given—a heroine in Scotland is not necessarily a heroine in England. And would you call a suffragette a heroine?

1. Who was 'Kate Barlass', and what sacrifice did she make in vain?

2. How did a Glasgow woman, Mary Drummond, achieve the title of General?

3. Flora Macdonald was involved in two risings. In the first she was 'agin the Government'. In the second she was for the Government. In both she was on the defeated side. What were the two risings?

4. Where is the Maiden's Leap, and what is the romantic story behind the name?

5. Which of these five Scottish heroines never, in fact, existed: Jean Armour; Jeanie Deans; Catherine Douglas; Flora Macdonald; Annie Laurie?

6. Why did 'Black Agnes' dust the battlements of Dunbar Castle with her handkerchief?

7. Who is regarded in Scotland as the feminine equivalent of David Livingstone?

8. Where is there a permanent collection of mementoes of the suffragette campaign in Scotland?

9. What girl with a big mouth has become the heroine of two Scottish plays?

10. Who was caged because she took part in a crowning?

Answers on pages 154–155

Scotland possesses almost every form of transport that there is—except camels, possibly! Here are ten questions about transport by land, sea, and air. Mountains and long sea lochs make the West of Scotland in particular a real headache to transport experts. And there are people in the Western Isles who know all about aeroplanes, yet have never travelled in a train.

1. How many airports are there in Scotland?

2. It cost £3,000,000 and took 5,000 men seven years to build it. Even now it takes thirty-five men three years to paint it. What is it?

3. If you look at a map you'll see that Loch Lomond and Loch Long are completely separate. How did the Vikings get their galleys from one to the other 700 years ago?

4. You know that a number of athletes have broken the Four Minute Mile. What would you think of their chances if they had to run a Scots mile?

5. Where and when was the first railway built in Scotland?

6. The shortest regular passenger air flight in the world is in Scotland. Can you say where?

7. How would you travel down 'Neptune's Staircase'?

8. Can you still get the 'Shetland Bus'?

9. When and where did the first Scottish passenger steamer sail?

10. Four famous trains, the Heart of Midlothian, the Flying Scotsman, the Queen of Scots and the Royal Scot, ran from Scotland to London. Which, if any, of them are still running?

QUIZ NO. 42 *VARIORUM*

'Life is all a variorum,' said the Bard. So you can guess that a Variorum is a very mixed bag. Up to now each of my quizes has dealt with one single subject. But here are ten questions which deal with anything at all. Most of them have been chosen because they are rather quirky questions, so watch out!

1. Where is the Electric Brae, and why is it so called?

2. What high office does the 37th Chief of the Clan MacLean hold, and what was his connection with the wedding of Prince Charles to Lady Diana?

3. Of what town was it said that there was as much of it under the ground as there was above it?

4. The Trossachs are famous for scenery. But what does the name mean?

5. Which Scottish village is said to be the birthplace of Pontius Pilate?

6. Of what Scottish author was it written:

> O'er all the Bards together put
> From Friockheim to Japan,
> He towers above, beyond dispute,
> Creation's greatest man.

7. Which two English Kings are supposed to have really lived in Scotland?

8. To what island do people sail to see the Cave Picture? And what is its subject?

9. Gretna Green is still the Mecca of eloping couples. Where was the eastern equivalent of Gretna Green?

10. What was odd (or do I mean even?) about the house at John o' Groats, and who was John?

[73] *Answers on pages 158–159*

THE FAR CORNERS OF THE EARTH

Scotsmen have always been great explorers. Although they retain a fierce love of their native land, they like to leave it quite early in life. This quiz deals mainly with Scotsmen who got there first! When I say 'first', I mean first as far as what we call the civilized world is concerned. The natives were there all the time.

1. Who was the first white man to cross Canada, and how did he leave his mark?

2. The interior of a Continent was practically unknown until Mungo Park went into it. Which Continent, and what mystery was Mungo trying to solve?

3. The first man to cross Africa from west to east is remembered by most people for a much-quoted saying. Who was he, and what did he discover in South-East Africa?

4. You've heard often enough of Robert Bruce, but what did James Bruce do?

5. Maybe this man didn't do any actual exploring, but he certainly opened up a country. If you place his work across the Atlantic, you're maybe on the right lines.

6. Perhaps you've solved Question No. 1 and know who was the first white man to cross Canada. Now can you say who was the first white man to cross Australia from south to north?

7. How did Calgary in Canada get its name?

8. The most famous detective agency in the world was founded by a man from the Gorbals of Glasgow. Who was he?

9. Why is the state capital of Western Australia called Perth, and the state capital of Queensland called Brisbane?

10. Who was the Scot who led the first expedition to make contact with the Grand Lama of Tibet?

Scot led first expedition to Tibet — see question 10.

Answers on page 160

QUIZ NO. 44 *WHAT'S MY NUMBER?*

The questions in this section range through Scottish geography, history, and a few more subjects, but they have one thing in common. Each is connected with a number. Sometimes you have to find your answer from the number I give you. Sometimes the answer is the number.

1. How many times did unlucky Berwick change hands before Richard Crookback finally captured it for England in 1482?

2. How many Members of Parliament represent Scotland in the House of Commons?

3. Where will you find the Five Sisters of Kintail?

4. How many islands are there in the Shetland group: (a) 20; (b) 50; (c) 100? And can you say how many of these are inhabited?

5. Who were the Seven Men of Moidart?

6. What is 'The Glorious Twelfth'?

7. A Lord Provost in Scotland is the equivalent of a Lord Mayor in England. How many Lord Provosts are there in Scotland, and with what cities are they associated?

8. How many rivers in Scotland are named the Esk, and where are they?

9. The Celtic bard Ossian knew the Three Sisters well. Where would you go to find them?

10. What's odd about the Twelve Apostles of Holywood?

I am well aware that claiming that any invention was absolutely the first of its kind is a risky business. For one thing, the Russians have brought up a lot of 'firsts' to disprove British and American claims to have invented or discovered this, that or the other. As far as I know, however, these are genuine Scottish firsts.

1. Who was the Scot who invented a calculating machine, the first battle tank, and logarithms?

2. A pioneer of television carried out experiments with a musical comedy and film star in the Manse of Helensburgh. Who was he?

3. Whose invention was worth at least a penny-farthing?

4. A Scot with a strong river connection perfected the compass and pioneered the cable. Who was he, and which particular cable was involved?

5. Who was walking across Glasgow Green on a Sunday when he got an idea that speeded up the world?

6. Our last quiz was called 'What's My Number?' Which Scotsman had the best right to ask that question?

7. Rowland Hill gets all the credit for the penny post, but who first suggested adhesive stamps?

8. Can you name the Ayrshire man who made himself a hat out of wood and was the first to light his house with gas?

[77]

9. And who is the Ayrshire man whose invention is still called by his own name? He might well be called the Colossus of Roads.

10. What have James Clerk Maxwell and R. A. Watson-Watt in common?

An Ayrshire pioneer — see question 8.

We use, in conversation and writing, a great many phrases from other countries. Many are from the French (particularly in Scotland, because of the Auld Alliance), and even more nowadays are from America. Scotland, too, has given a number of phrases to the world at large, though some of them seem, at first blush, to have no relation to Scotland at all.

1. 'True blue' sounds as English as can be, but it actually comes from some dissenting Scots. Who were they, and how did 'true blue' originate?

2. Probably the most often sung line (and the most often mispronounced too!) in the English-speaking world is 'For auld lang syne'. What does it mean, and where does it come from?

3. What words did the old Carron Company of Falkirk give to the English language?

4. What is 'an auld wife's tale'?

5. Why would you not relish being tried by 'Jeddart justice'?

6. How did a 'rider-out' get that name?

7. Would you welcome a 'lad o' pairts' to your home?

8. You probably know that whisky is called 'John Barleycorn'. But do you know why?

9. What would you do with 'The Devil's Books'?

10. Most people who talk about pedigrees are referring to dogs or cats. But to whom should a 'lang pedigree' be applied?

   Answers on page 165

From time to time I've mentioned 'The Auld Alliance'—the traditional friendship between Scotland and France. It flourished most when wars were going on between England and the Continent. On the active side, its last fling was when France helped Prince Charles Edward Stewart in the 1745 rising. By the time that Napoleon was threatening Britain, the Auld Alliance had so far faded that Scots rushed to volunteer to fight against France.

1. When did the Auld Alliance start?

2. What famous Edinburgh street cry (used today as the title of a students' magazine) is a corruption of the French?

3. What has haggis to do with the Auld Alliance?

4. Here are three French words—*gauche, gentil, bien.* The Scottish versions of these words are in common use today. What are they?

5. Who were the first Scots Guards?

6. What tea-table delicacy, assumed today to be typically Scottish, was actually brought to Scotland from France?

7. You may hear someone say in Scotland, 'Aye, he's a dour man, but his wife is very douce.' How would a knowledge of French help you to find out what was meant?

8. And what would a Scottish housewife mean if she cried to her daughter, 'Bring the ashets out of the aumrie'?

9. Where is Little France in Scotland?

10. Most Scotswomen in a butcher's shop would ask for a leg of mutton by a French name. What is the name?

QUIZ NO. 48 *MEN MUST WORK*

The Scots have always been known as hard workers. Scottish engineers have taken ships all over the world. Scots have pioneered roads and railways. Scots still manage tea and rubber plantations, and sink oil wells, and put up buildings in countries far distant from Scotland. But what do the Scots do in Scotland?

1. Everybody knows the Clyde is famous for shipbuilding, but what part of it is famous for shipbreaking?

2. Which Scottish towns are famous for: *(a)* silk; *(b)* lace; *(c)* tweed; *(d)* knitwear; *(e)* linoleum; *(f)* jute?

3. The biggest clock in the world was on the tower of a factory in the South-West of Scotland. Which factory was this and what did it make?

4. What part of Scotland did the Thames Embankment come from?

5. What was the 'improver' invented by David Dale for his spinning mills?

6. What connection have the Gourock Ropeworks with captains and clowns?

7. Arran Chiefs and Arran Banners go all over the world. What good do they do?

8. What is the biggest single export industry in Scotland?

9. Which Scottish industry is unique?

10. What have Dounreay, Loch Sloy and Hunterston in common?

You will know by now what a 'lad o' pairts' is. This quiz is not only about clever men who have got on in the world, but also about education in Scotland. John Knox, generally regarded as a church reformer and stern critic of other people's morals, is seldom remembered for the fact that he demanded a school in every parish. He could be fairly termed the founder of the Scottish educational system.

1. Scotland has four universities which are older than any in Britain, with the exception of Oxford and Cambridge. Can you name them and put them in the order of their foundation?

2. Two Glasgow men founded an Academy of Arts years before the Royal Academy was founded in London. Who were they, and for what other reason were they famous?

3. What renowned work of reference is often called 'Murray's Dictionary', and why?

4. Glasgow High School gave Britain two Prime Ministers, and Hutcheson's Grammar School in Glasgow gave Canada a Governor-General. Can you name these three former pupils?

5. What world-famous discoveries were made by (a) Joseph Lister; (b) Sir Ronald Ross; (c) Sir Alexander Fleming?

6. J. M. Barrie, a 'lad o' pairts' himself, wrote a play called *The Admirable Crichton*. Who was the real Admirable Crichton and what did he do?

7. Can you name the Scot who gave London three of its most famous bridges, and the Scot who gave Wales two of its most famous bridges?

8. Church ministers of all denominations use a work that was composed by a Scotsman. Can you say what it is, and who is the author?

9. The man who made 'Self Help' a household word was born in Scotland. Who was he, and where was he born?

10. Which Canadian University was founded by a man who emigrated from Glasgow?

Time for discovery? See question 5.

Answers on page 170

QUIZ NO. 50   *A GAITHER-UP*

A 'gaither-up' is exactly what it says it is—a gathering up of whatever happens to be lying around. In preparing this selection of quizzes, I collected a great deal of material. And, although I have now asked you 490 questions, I have one or two left over that I rather like.

1. Which joint founder of an Oxford College also founded Sweetheart Abbey in Dumfriesshire? And why is it called Sweetheart Abbey?

2. What Scottish leader of a lost cause pretended to be a colleen to avoid capture?

3. Where is the Prentice Pillar, and what is its tragic tale?

4. Who was the 'Burns of the North', and what marked him out from most poets?

5. James IV marooned two infants with a dumb nurse on Inchkeith, an island in the Firth of Forth, in order to discover what language they would speak. What language did they speak when rescued?

6. What have the 'Lantern of the North' and the 'Lamp of the Lothian' in common?

7.
   Which English football team plays in the Scottish Cup?

8. Do you think you should avoid the Edinburgh Ell?

9. Where will you find Moscow and Rome in Scotland?

10. Would you like to join 'The Merry Dancers'?

ANSWERS

1. The patron saint of Scotland is St. Andrew, supposedly the only saint who was crucified on a diagonal cross. Russia, in olden days, had also St. Andrew as its patron saint.

2. The estimated population of Scotland is 5,500,000.

3. The national emblem of Scotland is the thistle—not the sort of thistle you see growing in fields everywhere in Britain, but a particulary tall and prickly one. Scotch thistles on show in Edinburgh are over six feet in height. The lion rampant is the emblem of the monarch of Scotland.

4. The ministers and elders of the Church of Scotland meet once a year in the Assembly Hall in Edinburgh to discuss life and work in Scotland, and confer on matters of world interest.

5. There are thirty-two counties in Scotland.

6. The area of Scotland is 30,405 square miles.

7. James VI of Scotland became James I of Britain when he succeeded to the throne of England in 1603. This was the Union of the Crowns. The Scottish and English Parliaments were not united until 1707.

8. The coast of Scotland is so indented by sea lochs (the equivalent of Norwegian fiords) that the farthest you can get away from salt water is thirty-nine miles.

9. Seven Scottish mountains are over 4,000 feet. They are Ben Nevis (4,406); Ben Macdhui (4,296); Braeriach (4,248); Cairn Toul (4,241); Cairngorm (4,084); Aonach Beag

(4,060); Carn Mor Dearg (4,012). Ben Nevis, of course, is
the highest mountain in Britain.

10. A Sassenach (or some Gaelic experts say 'Sasunnach') is
a foreigner to Scotland, but the word is usually applied in a
half-affectionate, half-teasing way to English visitors.

1. The Cobbler is the popular name for Ben Arthur, the highest (2,891 feet) mountain of the Arrochar Alps. From the village of Arrochar at the head of Loch Long you see the topmost point of Ben Arthur looking like a cobbler bending over his last.

2. The Duke of Argyll's Bowling Green is a group of high mountains in the peninsula of Ardgoil, bounded by Loch Long on the east and Loch Goil on the west. The description was coined by Highlanders to show what doughty men the Dukes of Argyll were.

3. From Goatfell on the Isle of Arran in the Firth of Clyde you can see 126 other mountains. Goatfell is 2,866 feet and is the highest mountain on Arran. Near its peak a famous Victorian murder took place, when a Scot, James Laurie, murdered an Englishman, Edwin Rose, and concealed the body under a boulder in the Corrie of Fire.

4. Ben Nevis, at 4,406 feet the highest mountain in Britain. The description is a geologist's.

5. The best mountaineering in Britain is to be had on the Coolins (or Cuillins) in the Isle of Skye. There are more than a score of peaks, and at least seven of these exceed 3,000 feet in height.

6. The difference between Tee and Hee is a mere 92 feet. Ben Tee (known as Glengarry's Bowling Green) is by Glengarry and is 2,956 feet. Ben Hee, at 2,864 feet, is the highest point of Reay Forest, Sutherland.

7. MacLeod's Tables are two flat-topped hills which dominate the Peninsula of Quirinish in the Isle of Skye. They are 1,538 and 1,601 feet. It is said that a MacLeod chieftain

entertained one of the Kings of Scotland to dinner on top of the higher Table.

8. Munro's Tables, published by the Scottish Mountaineer-eering Club, are a list of Scottish peaks over 3,000 feet, tabulated by Professor Munro.

9. The Cairngorm Mountains form the most extensive area of Britain at an elevation of over 3,000 feet. They include six peaks of over 4,000 feet.

10. The top of Ben Lawers, on the north side of Loch Tay, is known as 'The Botanist's Paradise' because a variety of rare Alpine plants is seen here which cannot be found else-where in Britain. It is the only British habitat of *Saxifraga cernua*.

1. No, it's not Glencoe. It's Glen Fruin, running inland from Gareloch in the Firth of Clyde. The MacGregors massacred the Colquhouns in a Clan battle there in 1603, and as a result the MacGregors were outlawed and their name proscribed.

2. The longest glen in Scotland is Glen Lyon, Perthshire—approximately thirty miles. The Great Glen (Glen More) is not, properly speaking, a glen at all.

3. The road up Glen Croe from Loch Long to the Rest and Be Thankful rises from sea level to 860 feet. When General Wade's roadmakers reached the top, they erected a stone with the inscription which gives the summit of the glen its name.

4. Prince Charles Edward Stewart raised his father's standard in Glenfinnan, at the head of Loch Shiel, on 19th August 1745, and so started the venture of the '45.

5. King Robert the Bruce fought his first real battle against English troops in Glen Trool, Kirkcudbrightshire. His heavily outnumbered forces won and his venture, unlike Bonnie Prince Charlie's, was a success.

6. If you're a golfer, you should have got this one. It's Gleneagles, Perthshire, which has a luxury hotel and three golf courses—the King's and the Queen's for the tigers and the Wee for the rabbits.

7. The most famous whisky in Scotland is made at Glenlivet Distillery, founded by George Smith in 1824. It is the only distillery in the glen, but the name Glenlivet is added to twenty-six other whiskies distilled in the Strathspey and Speyside districts. So Glenlivet goes all over the world, on bottle labels.

[91]

8. You really know your Scottish history if you got this one. The Battle of Glen Shiel was fought in June 1719, when General Wightman and English troops defeated a mixed force of Highlanders and Spaniards. Some 400 Spaniards landed in Loch Alsh from two frigates, all that was left of an invasion fleet of thirty ships. The Highlanders took to the hills, and the Spaniards surrendered.

9. Glen Avon is the scene of most of the action of *The Small Dark Man*, by Maurice Walsh. Glen Quharity is often mentioned in the 'Thrums' books by J. M. Barrie. In Glen Clunie road, Braemar, a house is marked by a tablet recording the fact that here R. L. Stevenson wrote *Treasure Island*.

10. Scotland's most tragic glen is, of course, Glencoe, where the Campbells massacred the MacDonalds on the 13th February 1692. The reason, however, that thousands visit Glencoe every spring is that it is now a ski-ing centre and the first ski lift in Scotland has been built there.

ANSWERS TO QUIZ NO. 4

1. Bonnie Prince Charlie's full name was Charles Edward Louis Philip Casimir Stewart.

2. The Jacobites were named after Prince Charles's father, James II (deposed in 1688). 'Jacobus' is the Latin for James. The Jacobites were given their name in the rising of 1715. Non-Jacobites refer to the '15 and the '45 as rebellions.

3. Prince Charles made his first landing in Scotland at Borradale, from the French frigate *La Doutelle*, on 25th July 1745. When his cause had failed, he was taken off at the same place by *L'Heureux*, on 20th September 1746. The first voyage was from France, the second to France.

4. Prince Charles marched his army over the 'New Road', made by General Wade in 1735. It runs up the Spey valley and crosses the Pass of Corrieyairack to Glen Tarff and Fort Augustus. It is twenty-four miles long and rises to 2,507 feet. It still exists, but is now derelict.

5. The Clan MacDougall had been punished for joining in the rising of 1715. When the '45 came along, the Chief's wife was determined that he should not join Prince Charles. So she poured boiling water over his feet and pretended it was an accident. He was so crippled that he could not go an' fecht for Chairlie!

6. When the Battle of Culloden took place on 16th April 1746 both Prince Charles and the Duke of Cumberland (third son of George II), the rival commanders, were twenty-five years old.

7. 'Black Friday', 6th December 1745, was the day that London heard the news that Prince Charles had reached Derby.

[93]

8.   Prince Charles slept in Flora Macdonald's house at Kingsburgh on the Isle of Skye. Many years later the sheets from his bed were used as shrouds for Flora Macdonald and her mother-in-law.

9.   Flora Macdonald and her husband entertained Dr. Johnson and James Boswell at Kingsburgh on 12th September 1773, and Dr. Johnson slept in Prince Charlie's bed.

10.   'God Save the King' was first sung in public in the Drury Lane Theatre, London, on September 18th 1745, when Bonnie Prince Charlie's army was approaching Derby and seemed likely to attack London. One of the verses never sung now is violently anti-Jacobite.

ANSWERS TO QUIZ NO. *5*

1. Loch Lomond can be said to surround a foot. The Scottish word for island is 'inch', and there are twelve inches in Loch Lomond. Among them are Inchlonaig, Inchtavannach, Inchconnachan, Inchcruin, Inchfad, Inchmoan, Inchcailloch and Inchmurrin.

2   Loch Leven, Kinross-shire. Mary Queen of Scots was imprisoned in Loch Leven Castle on one of the eleven islands from 17th June 1567 until 2nd May 1568. On another island is the Priory of St. Serf.

3. Lochnagar—the 'Dark Lochnagar' of Lord Byron's poem. It means 'the goat's lake' and it is situated at the foot of the north-east precipices of Lochnagar (3,786 feet), the highest point of Balmoral Forest.

4. The usual answer to this question is one—the Lake of Menteith, in the Rob Roy country. Its largest island is Inchmahome, where Mary Queen of Scots took refuge when she was five, and where R. B. Cunninghame Graham is buried. But there is also a piece of water formed by damming in East Lothian called Prestmennan Lake.

5. The Nor' Loch in Edinburgh was drained and made into the main railway line to Glasgow and the beautiful Princes Street Gardens.

6. Loch Faskally, famous for its salmon ladder, was made by damming the River Garry at Pitlochry, the geographical centre of Scotland.

7. Holy Loch is said to have got its name from the foundering there of a ship bringing soil from the Holy Land to be used by St. Mungo for the foundation of Glasgow Cathedral. A less romantic story is that it comes from the presence there of a holy man, St. Mun.

[95]

8.   Loch Nevis ('Heaven') and Loch Hourn ('Hell') run into the Sound of Sleat between the mainland and the Isle of Skye. They are separated by mountainous Knoydart.

9.   Loch Morar, between Arisaig and Mallaig, is a freshwater loch more than 1,000 feet deep.

10.   There are supposed to be monsters in Loch Hourn and Loch Morar. Two ministers and several other people saw The Beast in Loch Hourn in 1872 and it has been seen since. The Loch Morar monster is not so well authenticated, but it is known affectionately as Morag, just as the Loch Ness monster is called Nessie.

1. Powsowdie is sheep's-head broth. Howtowdie and cock-a-leekie are both soups made from fowls, but in the case of cock-a-leekie the fowl is boiled with leeks. Partan bree is crab soup—literally crab (partan) brew (bree).

2. Scotland is traditionally 'The Land o' Cakes' because of the high reputation of its housewives for baking.

3. Mrs. Macnab was one of them. She was the wife of a farmer living near Ballater in the time of Queen Victoria. She was so renowned as a baker that King Frederick of Prussia, and other noble guests at Balmoral Castle, went frequently to have tea with her and taste her scones.

4. A scone is baked from flour, baking soda, salt and milk or water. Scone is a place in Perthshire. It was formerly the capital of Scotland and many Scottish Kings were crowned there on the Stone of Scone (or Stone of Destiny). A scone is pronounced 'scawn', while Scone is pronounced 'Scoon'. Neither is pronounced 'scoan'.

5. Scots are apt to tease Sassenachs about the 'wild haggis' roaming round the mountains. It's actually made from sheep's lights, liver and heart, beef suet, onions and oatmeal, seasoned with salt and black pepper, and cooked in a sheep's stomach.

6. You always get haggis at a Burns Supper, and 'neeps' are turnips, while 'champit tatties' are mashed potatoes. If you thought 'neeps' were glasses of whisky, you're confusing that word with 'nips'. You sometimes get that with the haggis too.

7. Black Bun is made for the New Year festivities in Scotland. It is usually on display at Hogmanay (New Year's Eve) and goes well with whatever you happen to be drinking that night. It is a very rich cake made with all sorts of fruits and

nuts, with whisky, rum, or brandy added. So much fruit is used that the inside is actually black.

8.   Pheasant is the biggest of these game birds, grouse comes second, and partridge third.

9.   (a) Arbroath smokies (or smoked haddock); (b) Dundee cake; (c) Dunlop cheese; (d) Forfar bridies; (e) Loch Fyne herring or kippers; (f) Selkirk bannock.

10.   The 'Selkirk Grace' is supposed to have been first given by Robert Burns, but some authorities doubt whether or not he actually composed it. It runs:

> Some ha'e meat and cannae eat
> And some wad eat that want it.
> But we ha'e meat and we can eat,
> Sae let the Lord be thankit.

ANSWERS TO QUIZ NO. 7

1. Burns was born in a cottage built by his father at Alloway, near Ayr, on 25th January 1759.

2. When Burns's father built the cottage, it faced the main road from Ayr. Now the main road runs on the other side, so that the birthplace has now its back to the road.

3. The Mitchell Library in Glasgow, Scotland, has a collection of more than 3,500 volumes on Robert Burns and his works.

4. The first volume of poems by Robert Burns is entitled *Poems, Chiefly in the Scottish Dialect*, and it is known as the Kilmarnock Edition, as it was printed by John Wilson in that Ayrshire town in 1786.

5. The song which mentions Ailsa Craig, the 1,000-foot crag in the Firth of Clyde, is 'Duncan Gray'. The germane lines are:

> Duncan fleeched and Duncan prayed—
> Ha-ha, the wooing o't!
> Meg was deaf as Ailsa Craig—
> Ha-ha, the wooing o't!

6. The famous lines are:

> The best laid schemes o' mice an' men
> Gang aft agley.

They are from the poem: 'To a Mouse'.

7. The first line of 'The Cotter's Saturday Night' is 'My lov'd, my honor'd, much respected friend!' Of 'Tam o' Shanter'—'When chapman billies leave the street'. Of 'To a Mouse'—'Wee, sleekit, cowrin', tim'rous beastie.' Of 'To a Daisy'—Wee, modest, crimson tipped flow'r.'

[99]

8. Burns called himself Robert, Rob, Robin, and Rab, but never Rabbie. By Ayrshire tradition Rabbie is a name reserved for a fool. As far as is known, Rabbie in connection with Burns appears only once, on a Masonic apron, which was presented to him.

9. Jane, Duchess of Gordon, who introduced Robert Burns to the fashionable world in her Edinburgh salon, declared that his conversation carried her off her feet.

10. The dying saying attributed to Burns is, 'Don't let the awkward squad fire over my grave.' Burns was a member of the Dumfries Volunteers, and they took part in his funeral procession in July 1796.

1. *The Life of Johnson* was written by James Boswell; *The Wealth of Nations* by Adam Smith; *The French Revolution* by Thomas Carlyle; and *The Golden Bough* by Sir James Frazer.

2. When young J. M. Barrie went to Dumfries Academy he played Cowboys and Indians, and similar games, in the grounds of Moat Brae House, next door to the school. Later he said in Dumfries that many of his ideas for *Peter Pan* were born there.

3. The Island that likes to be visited—'six acres in area, uninhabited, a hundred yards from a greater island, quite close to the inn, near the whaling station, with firs, a few rowan trees, and a tiny pool out of which a stream flows'— is believed to be in West Loch Tarbert, Harris.

4. Henry Mackenzie (1745–1831) wrote a novel entitled *The Man of Feeling* and was thereafter known by that name. He was one of the intellectuals who welcomed Robert Burns to Edinburgh in 1786. Burns admired him greatly and Sir Walter Scott dedicated *Waverley* to him.

5. *(a)* Hugh MacDiarmid was Christopher M. Grieve; *(b)* Hugh Foulis was Neil Munro; *(c)* Saki was H. H. Munro; *(d)* Christopher North was Professor John Wilson; *(e)* James Bridie was Dr. Osborne H. Mavor.

6. George Blake, John Davidson, James Watt, and Captain Kidd were all born in Greenock.

7. Sydney Smith, the English wit, said this of Thomas Carlyle and his wife, Jane Welsh.

8. Levenford (Cronin) is Dumbarton; Garvel (Blake) is Greenock; Thrums (Barrie) is Kirriemuir; and Dundon (Gibbon) is a compound of Aberdeen and Dundee.

9. *The Wind in the Willows* by Kenneth Grahame and *Treasure Island* by Robert Louis Stevenson.

10. R.L.S. said *Dr. Jekyll and Mr. Hyde* was based on Deacon William Brodie of Edinburgh. The Deacon lived a respectable life during the day, and became a dangerous criminal at night.

1. 'The Road to the Isles' is fifty-six miles long, from Invermoriston to Kyle of Lochalsh. Its first hiker was General Wade, who made it. But it was also followed by Dr. Johnson and Boswell in 1773.

2. Tam o' Shanter in Burns's poem. As he rode home on his grey mare Meg, he was . . .

> Whiles holding fast his gude blue bonnet;
> Whiles crooning o'er some auld Scots sonnet.

3. Many people think these songs are Scottish, but they're not. 'Jeanie with the light brown hair' is by the American Stephen Foster. 'I know where I'm going' is an old Irish song.

4. The standard was raised on the Braes o' Mar for James II in 1715. His son 'Chairlie', otherwise Prince Charles Edward Stewart, was not born until 1720, and didn't arrive in Scotland until 1745.

5. 'The tartan of Mary Houston' tells how Mary got a tartan pattern burned on her bare legs because she sat too close to the fire.

6. These lines are from 'Auld Lang Syne', by Robert Burns.

7. The song 'Loch Lomond' is about a Jacobite who was being executed at Carlisle. The Highlanders had a superstition that the spirit of a dead man travelled home under the earth, so that in this case the one who took 'the low road' would reach home sooner than his companion who rode home alive.

8. A ceilidh is an informal concert in the Highlands; a clarsach is the small Celtic harp; and a coronach is a funeral lament in the Highlands.

[103]

9. You don't walk at all. A waulking song is sung by women who are standing still as they 'waulk' or thicken cloth by handling.

10. 'Will ye no' come back again?' is the traditional Jacobite song of farewell to Bonnie Prince Charlie, when he sailed from Scotland in 1746. It is now used by the Scots as a farewell song to anyone they like very much.

ANSWERS TO QUIZ NO. 10

1. The Clan MacKay has a Dutch chief, Lord Reay. Their slogan is 'White Banner of The Mackay'.

2. The name Campbell comes from the Gaelic and means 'crooked mouth'. Cameron, also from the Gaelic, means 'crooked nose'.

3. Between Balmoral and the Iver Inn is the Cairn of Remembrance, rallying point of the Farquharson Clan before a battle. Each warrior contributed a stone to the cairn as they set out, and those that returned each took a stone away. The stones that were left represented the number of the slain.

4. The slogan of Clan Campbell is 'Cruachan', from Ben Cruachan. The Clan Buchanan slogan is 'Clar-Innis', which is an island in Loch Lomond.

5. The Clan MacCrimmon, hereditary pipers to the Clan MacLeod, maintained a famous college of piping at Boreraig, Skye, for more than 200 years. A memorial cairn is near the site of the college, and the land has been given to the Glasgow College of Piping for an annual rent of a pibroch and a penny. A MacCrimmon student had a seven-year course and had to learn nearly 300 pipe tunes by heart.

6. The MacGregors, whose name was proscribed, were led by Rob Roy to the Battle of Sheriffmuir in 1715. They were late in arriving, and held back until both sides left the field. Rob Roy got the spoils of battle, took what he wanted, and burned the remainder.

7. The Fairy Flag belongs to Clan MacLeod, and is kept at Dunvegan Castle, Skye. It's supposed to have the power, when waved, of saving the Clan from three great dangers. It has already been waved twice with success—once when the

MacLeods were hard pressed by Macdonalds, and secondly to end a cattle murrain.

8. The Fiery Cross was made of wood. The ends were seared in fire and then dipped in the blood of a goat killed by the Chief of the Clan. So, by the time it was carried round the countryside, the fire was out.

9. When Prince Charles and his Highland Army invested Glasgow in 1745, some of the Chiefs were for burning and looting the city. Cameron of Lochiel interceded on Glasgow's behalf, and the grateful magistrates said they would ring the Tolbooth chimes when Lochiel or his descendants visited the town.

10. The Clan MacKinnon's name derives from the Gaelic, 'Sons of the Seal'.

1. He who has decided to take a line of action is determined to take it. In other words, there's no arguing with an obstinate man.

2. In the face of worry or trouble, keep silent and keep calm

3. A small bush is better than no shelter at all. 'Better a wee bush than nae bield' was the motto of Robert Burns.

4. Take notice of (or pay attention to) time before you are in danger of losing it. Sometimes translated as: Take care of time ere time be taken.

5. Literally, we'll let that fly stick to the wall. We'll let that particular aspect of our argument drop in the meantime.

6. Do your work, but don't overdo it. In an industrial sense, however, 'ca' canny' means going warily or working slowly during a dispute.

7. You need a stout heart when you face a steep hill. In other words, take courage when facing adversity.

8. 'Cauld kale' is cold soup, and 'het again' is reheated, so this is reheated broth. It can be an old love affair rekindled, a worn-out argument revived, or an old sermon preached yet again, among other things.

9. You may have lost an opportunity, but if a friend of yours gets it you should be as glad as though you'd got it yourself.

10. 'A causey saint an' kitchen deil' is the type of person who behaves well in the outside world but very badly at home. Literally, a street saint and a kitchen devil.

1. *(a)* The Doonhamers - Queen of the South; *(b)* The Red Lichties - Arbroath; *(c)* The Jags - Partick Thistle; *(d)* The Spiders - Queen's Park; *(e)* The Bairns - Falkirk; *(f)* The Bully Wee - Clyde; *(g)* The Steel Men - Motherwell; *(h)* The Sons of the Rock - Dumbarton; *(i)* The Honest Men - Ayr United.

2. Try to get out of it, or blast your way out if you had the right lie! Hell is a bunker on the Old Course, St. Andrews.

3. There are more than 250 first-class golf courses in Scotland.

4. The oldest horse race in the world is claimed to be the one for working horses held at the Marymass Races in Irvine every August. It was first run in the twelfth century.

5. Paradise is the nickname for the Celtic Football Club's ground at Parkhead, Glasgow. There is occasionally trouble when Celtic meet Rangers and the battle of the 'Old Firm' arouses violent emotions.

6. (*a*) Benny Lynch—world boxing champion; (*b*) K. J. Scotland—Rugby Union football international; (*c*) Ian Peebles—Scot who played cricket for England; (*d*) Ian Black —European champion swimmer; (*c*) Eric Liddell—Olympic Games champion sprinter; (*f*) Eric Brown—golfer who played for Britain.

7. The Scottish 'Wimbledon' is at Craiglockhart, Edinburgh; the Scottish 'Lord's' at Raeburn Place, Edinburgh; the Scottish 'Ascot' at Ayr Racecourse; and the Scottish 'Cowes' at Hunter's Quay during the Clyde Fortnight.

8. The Royal Company of Archers.

[108]

9. No, it's not St. Andrews, though that's the Royal and Ancient. It's the Gentlemen Golfers, now known as the Honourable Company of Edinburgh Golfers, founded in 1744.

10. (*a*) The Calcutta Cup is for the Rugby Union match between Scotland and England; (*b*) The Scottish Cup is our equivalent of the F.A. Cup in England; (*c*) The Craw's Nest Tassie is for the winner of a golf tournament held at Carnoustie; (*d*) The Camanachd Cup is presented to the winning shinty team in Scotland.

1. They are fishes. The powan is the freshwater herring of Loch Lomond, and the vendace is a small fish of the salmon family found only in Castle Loch, near Lochmaben.

2. It is Meikleour Beech Hedge, near Perth. The beech trees have been planted so as to grow together in the form of a hedge.

3. A partan is the Scottish name for a crab; a foumart is a polecat; a tod is a fox; and a brock is a badger.

4. An inscribed stone at Loth, in Sutherland, commemorates the slaying of the last wolf in Scotland in 1700.

5. The churchyard yew at Fortingall, at the entrance to Glen Lyon, is claimed to be more than 3,000 years old and the oldest tree in Europe.

6. The three Gaelic 'worthies of the ocean' are the seal, the lobster, and the mackerel.

7. A gillie was once the personal servant to a Highland chief but now he is a professional attendant and helper to sportsmen who go out fishing or shooting. A garron is a small but strong Highland pony. So you can make your choice!

8. The island of St. Kilda (or Hirta), forty miles west of North Uist in the Atlantic, is the only known home of the St. Kilda wren, the St. Kilda mouse, and the St. Kilda field-mouse.

9. The deer forest country of Scotland covers more than 2,500,000 acres. The strange thing about a Scottish deer 'forest' is that there is usually more bare mountain than trees in it.

10. A royal stag carries twelve points on its horns.

ANSWERS TO QUIZ NO. 14

1. Malcolm III of Scotland. He was known as Malcolm Canmore, and Canmore is derived from the Gaelic for 'Big Head'.

2. King Edgar of England made a present of a palace in London to King Kenneth II of Scotland. On the site of that palace is New Scotland Yard.

3. The last King of Scotland to speak the Gaelic was James IV. His seven other languages included English, Latin, French, German, Flemish, Italian, and Spanish.

4. (a) James II died when a cannon exploded beside him during a siege; (b) James III was stabbed by a man who pretended to be a priest; (c) James I was murdered by a group of noblemen; (d) Alexander III fell over a cliff when his horse was frightened in a thunderstorm.

5. Toom Tabard means 'empty coat', and it was applied by the Scots to John Baliol because he had to do what Edward I of England told him.

6. Robert the Bruce, when he heard Edward I declare in London that he was going to invade Scotland, fled to his own country because he was a claimant to the Scottish throne and was afraid of arrest by Edward.

7. In the reign of James II the Scottish Parliament passed an Act which proclaimed that 'the football and the golf are to be utterly cried down'. This was because James II wanted his subjects to devote their leisure to military training, particularly archery. The other spoilsport was James VI, who, in his *Counterblast to Tobacco*, described it as 'black, stinking fume, loathsome to the eye, hateful to the nose, harmful to the brain, dangerous to the lungs'.

8. Robert the Bruce. His body is buried in Dunfermline Abbey, and his heart rests in Melrose Abbey. When he died, he asked Sir James Douglas to take his heart to the Holy Land. But Douglas was killed on the way, and Bruce's heart was brought back to Scotland.

9. The Prince of Wales in Scotland has the titles of Duke of Rothesay, Earl of Carrick, and Baron Renfrew.

10. 'The Hammer of the Scots' was the Edward I of England mentioned twice already in these answers. He took the Stone of Destiny, on which the Scottish Kings were crowned, from Scotland to London. His son, Edward II, promised to send it back, but never did.

ANSWERS TO QUIZ NO. 15

1. Mary Queen of Scots spent her last night (15th May 1568) on Scottish soil at Dundrennan Abbey, Auchencairn. She was taken to imprisonment in England, and was executed many years later.

2. The oldest building in Edinburgh is St. Margaret's Chapel, the first structure you encounter when you enter Edinburgh Castle. St. Margaret, Queen of Malcolm Canmore, died in the Castle in 1093, and this eleventh-century building was named after her.

3. The first King of Britain, James VI of Scotland and I of England, was the son of Mary Queen of Scots. She gave birth to James in Edinburgh Castle on 19th June 1566.

4. Her Majesty Queen Elizabeth owns Balmoral Castle and Birkhall, near by, and also the Palace of Holyroodhouse in Edinburgh. Queen Elizabeth the Queen Mother owns the Castle of Mey, not far from Thurso.

5. The Queen Mother, when she was Duchess of York, gave birth to Princess Margaret at Glamis Castle in 1930. Macbeth (died 1057) was Thane of Glamis.

6. Princess Margaret, Maid of Norway, succeeded to the Throne of Scotland when she was three years of age. She died before reaching Scotland.

7. James V was referring to the Stewart line as Kings of Scotland. It came with Marjorie Bruce, daughter of Robert the Bruce, whose son by a Stewart was the first of the line. It ended with James V's daughter, Mary Queen of Scots, for her son became King of Britain.

8. Queen Victoria's father, the Duke of Kent, was Colonel of the Royal Scots at the time of her birth, so 'The Daughter of the Regiment' was played in her honour.

[113]

9. A regular user of the ferry, some 800 years before the Forth Bridge was built, was St. Margaret, wife of Malcolm Canmore.

10. She was born in Linlithgow Palace, but was carried to France when a child.

1. King Edwin of Northumbria (where Newcastle and district folk are known as 'Geordies') captured the Rock early in the seventh century. He fortified it and a town was built round the castle called Edwin's Burgh.

2. James IV of Scotland. Since his reign, Edinburgh has been regarded as the Capital.

3. Edinburgh earned its title of 'The Modern Athens' because of its history as a cultural centre and the many similarities in the natural setting of the two cities. 'Auld Reekie' refers to the smoke veil discharged from innumerable chimneys.

4. The Scott Monument was designed by a shepherd-boy turned architect, George Meikle Kemp. He was drowned in the Union Canal shortly before the inauguration of the monument in 1844.

5. The Palace of Holyroodhouse contains a picture gallery with 110 imaginary portraits of Scottish Kings executed by a Dutch artist, Jacob de Witt, to the order of Charles II. He was paid £120 a year for the two years he worked. This works out at a portrait every six and a half days at £2 3s. 8d. each.

6. The Royal Mile runs from Edinburgh Castle to the Palace of Holyroodhouse, and comprises the Castle Esplanade, Castlehill, Lawnmarket, High Street, and Canongate.

7. The Floral Clock contains more than 14,000 plants, and was first planted in 1903.

8. Henry VIII wanted Queen Mary to marry his son, the Prince of Wales. His 'Rough Wooing', to persuade her to say yes, consisted of attacking Scotland. Twice he sacked

Edinburgh, which had to be almost entirely rebuilt after Mary came to Holyroodhouse in 1561.

9. Beneath the lion-like mass of Arthur's Seat are resting King Arthur and the Knights of the Round Table.

10. Edinburgh Zoo has the largest collection of penguins of any zoo in the world. The number varies, but is generally between sixty and seventy.

ANSWERS TO QUIZ NO. 17

1. Birmingham (1,065,527); Glasgow (763,162); Liverpool (503,722); Edinburgh (446,361); Dundee (179,634).

2. *(a)* The oldest part of Glasgow Cathedral is early twelfth century; *(b)* Glasgow University was founded in 1451; *(c)* The Tolbooth tower at Glasgow Cross is all that remains of the prison. It was built in 1626; *(d)* The oldest house is Provand's Lordship, opposite the Cathedral. It was built about 1470.

3. (*a*) The Hielan'man's Umbrella is the railway bridge that takes trains from the Central Station over Argyle Street. Underneath this wide bridge Highlanders exiled in Glasgow used to meet regularly; (*b*) The Barrows form a second-hand market off the Gallowgate and get the name because, originally, the goods for sale were displayed on barrows instead of stalls; (*c*) The Butts is the Glasgow name for the Fire Brigade.

4. Queen's Park provided the whole Scottish side against England in Glasgow at the first international in 1872. The result was a goalless draw.

5. The Gorbals has inspired the novel *No Mean City*; the play *The Gorbals Story*; the film of the same name; and the ballet *Miracle in the Gorbals*.

6. In Kelvingrove Park, Glasgow, stands the duplicate of a bronze group of tigress and cubs on display in Central Park, New York. W. S. Kennedy of New York presented each group to the respective cities.

7. When World War One broke out a London reporter heard soldiers embarking on a trooper for France singing

S.F.F.—B   [117]

'Tipperary'. He wrote about it and the song became world famous. The men he heard were the Highland Light Infantry from Glasgow, and *they* had heard Florrie Forde sing this song (by Jack Judge of Liverpool) when they were on holiday in Douglas, Isle of Man, in July 1914.

8. Whistler, the American who was accused of 'throwing a pot of paint in the public's face'.

9. The 'Glasgow School' of painters, including Sir John Lavery, Sir James Guthrie, E. A. Walton, Hornel, and McGregor.

10. The Clyde at Glasgow Bridge was at one time so shallow that children could wade across it at low tide. Glasgow employed James Watt and Joseph Golborne to deepen the river, and it was made into a tidal canal. When big ships could come into the centre of Glasgow, trade flourished so much that the Clyde made the city rich.

1. The prototype of Robinson Crusoe (hero of Daniel Defoe's book as well as of modern pantomime) was Alexander Selkirk, son of a Largo shoemaker, who was marooned on the island of Juan Fernandez for five years. His statue in Largo is placed in front of the site where his house stood.

2. The statue of Marshal Keith stands in front of Peterhead Town House. He was born at Inverugie Castle, near Peterhead, and exiled after the '15 rising. He served in the Spanish and Russian armies, and was made a Field Marshal by Frederick the Great. Frederick's descendant, William I, gave the statue as a tribute to Keith.

3. You're wrong if you said Edinburgh. The first statue to Scott was erected in George Square, Glasgow, in 1837, five years after he died. It is by James Greenshields and stands on an eighty-foot column.

4. Yes, George Square, Glasgow, again. Including Scott, there are twelve statues in the Square, as well as the Cenotaph commemorating both World Wars.

5. The statue which dominates Elgin is that of the last Duke of Gordon.

6. The statue of Thomas Carlyle looks down the main street of Ecclefechan, where he was born. It is a replica of the Carlyle statue on the Chelsea Embankment, except for the fact that the Ecclefechan coat is longer than the Chelsea coat. This may be because some people fancy it's colder in Scotland!

7. The statue of Sir William Wallace in Aberdeen has one hand outflung in such a way that it is pointing directly at the door to the pit-stalls of His Majesty's Theatre.

8. Highland Mary (Mary Campbell) was born at Auchamore, Dunoon. Her statue has been placed so that she seems to be looking across the Firth of Clyde to Ayrshire, where she met and loved Robert Burns.

9. The dog is 'Greyfriars Bobbie' and the statue is near Greyfriars churchyard. When its master died, Bobbie refused to be taken away from the grave. Until the dog itself died, it remained at the graveside and was fed by local people.

10. Gladstone was fond of cutting down trees and so lost the third finger of his right hand. Thornycroft, the sculptor, in order to conceal this, made the statue so that Gladstone's right hand holds a book, and the stump is concealed in the leaves.

ANSWERS TO QUIZ NO. 19

1. The first monument to Lord Nelson was erected at Taynuilt even before his remains reached England. It was a large stone monolith dragged by workmen from Furnace to Taynuilt and inscribed, 'To the memory of Lord Nelson, this stone was erected by the Lorn Furnace workmen, 1805.' In the following year the first major monument to be erected to Lord Nelson was in Glasgow Green. It is a column 144 feet high.

2. The 'Pencil' is the local name for the pencil-shaped tower which commemorates the Battle of Largs, 1263, when the Scots drove the Vikings from their shores.

3. The largest monument to one man is the Wallace Monument at Causewayhead, near Stirling. It is a huge tower built on a rock known as the Abbey Craig.

4. The Scottish National War Memorial on Edinburgh Castle Rock includes white mice, carrier pigeons, and canaries, because they took part in the war effort. The Memorial, designed by Sir Robert Lorimer, was opened in 1927.

5. John Cobb was killed when attempting to break the world's water speed record on Loch Ness. The cairn has been built on the shore of the loch, near the spot where he died.

6. Seven brothers were entrusted by their eldest brother, laird of Invergarry, with the safe keeping of his son. They murdered the son, and were, in turn, killed and beheaded by Invergarry clansmen, who washed the seven heads in a well on the shore of Loch Oich before presenting them to the laird.

7. The Kitchener Memorial Tower in Orkney marks a place near that part of the sea where the *Hampshire* went down and Lord Kitchener was drowned.

8.   The Mausoleum at Hamilton was built by the 10th Duke of Hamilton in 1840. It included a chapel in which the echo was so great that it could not be used as a place of worship. The echo is still demonstrated to visitors, and has been recorded by the B.B.C.

9.   Henry Bell gets the credit for introducing the first practical steamboat to ply on European waters. It was the *Comet*, and it made regular voyages on the Firth of Clyde from 1812 to 1820. There are obelisks to Bell at Helensburgh and Dunglass Castle, and a memorial at Port Glasgow.

10.   The Commando Memorial is at Spean Bridge on the road from Fort William to Inverness. The Commandos did much of their training in this wild area.

1. The custom originates from the offerings which travellers once made in the Chapel of St. James before hazarding the dangerous crossing of the Forth by boat.

2. The Earl of Caithness and 300 Sinclairs crossed the Ord of Caithness on a Monday in 1513. Every one of them was killed at Flodden, and today superstitious Sinclairs believe they are courting fate if they cross the Ord on a Monday.

3. Edinburgh people spit on the Heart of Midlothian for luck. It is a heart-shaped formation of cobble-stones marking the site of the Old Tolbooth in the Royal Mile.

4. East Coast fishermen fear to meet a minister on the way to the boat, and most will turn back if they do. They also fear to speak of a salmon.

5. 'The Curse of Scotland' is the playing card the Nine of Diamonds. Among the many stories to account for this, my favourite is that it was on that card that the order for the Massacre of Glencoe was written.

6. A 'First Foot' is the first person to visit your house after the New Year has come in. He must be a dark man. Some people refuse to allow a fair-haired or red-haired man into the house until a dark man has entered first.

7. Highlanders believe that the horseshoe will prevent the infant being stolen by the Little Folk.

8. When you are taking your baby to be christened, you make up a 'Christening Piece'. This should contain some food (usually cake or dumpling) and a silver coin. You give the 'Christening Piece' to the first man you meet, if the baby is a girl, or to the first woman you meet, if the baby is a boy.

9. Widdershins means turning in the opposite direction to the sun. Very bad luck is supposed to come the way of a rider whose horse turns widdershins. (Witches always move widdershins when casting spells.)

10. Rags and pieces of cloth are tied to a tree by a well on Culloden field on 'Clootie Sunday' in May. Pennies are knocked into the Holy Tree at Loch Maree.

ANSWERS TO QUIZ NO. 21

1. 'Rule, Britannia' was written by James Thomson.

2. This is from a poem by Thomas Campbell on Lochiel. The germane lines are:

> 'Tis the evening of life lends me mystical lore,
> And coming events cast their shadows before.

3. These lines are from 'To a Louse, on seeing one in a Lady's bonnet', by Robert Burns.

4. Alexander Smith wrote this in *A Summer in Skye*.

5. James Boswell said this to Dr. Samuel Johnson on their first meeting. Dr. Johnson replied, 'That, sir, is what a very great many of your countrymen cannot help.'

6. R. L. Stevenson gave this description of 'Auld Reekie' in his *Edinburgh Picturesque Notes*.

7. These are the concluding words of the Arbroath Declaration made by the Parliament of Scotland meeting at Arbroath in April 1320.

8. So Neil Munro described Glencoe in his novel *John Splendid*.

9. This is the motto of the Keith family. It is carved over the doorway of Marischal College, Aberdeen, in the old Scots form: 'They haif said. Quhat say thay? Lat thame say.'

10. Sir James M. Barrie puts this into the mouth of his heroine in his play *What Every Woman Knows*.

ANSWERS TO QUIZ NO. 22

1. The River Clyde. It was famous for salmon fishing, especially in the upper reaches. When it gets to Glasgow there are shipbuilding yards, and when it reaches Greenock there are sugar refineries.

2. The Spey is the fastest river in Scotland. In some parts it is totally unnavigable.

3. Tay, 117 miles; Spey, 110 miles; Clyde, 106 miles; Tweed, 96 miles; Dee, 90 miles; Forth, 66 miles.

4. The Daer Water becomes the River Clyde at Water-meetings, near Elvanfoot. The River Beauly becomes the River Glass at Struy Bridge in Strath Glass.

5. The Rivers Murray, Murchison, and Lachlan are in Australia. Mackenzie, Fraser, and Hamilton are in Canada. All were named after Scotsmen who discovered them.

6. The Bridge of Teith, over the River Teith near Doune, was built by Robert Spittal, tailor to the Queen of James IV, in 1535 in order to spite a ferryman who had refused to ferry him across the Teith when he had left his purse behind.

7. These were the names of well-known River Clyde steamers in the heydey of 'Doon the Watter'.

8. Aberdeen is built mainly between the River Dee and the River Don.

9. (a) Pitlochry—Garry; (b) Brechin—South Esk; (c) Dumfries—Nith; (d) Balmoral—Dee; (e) Kelso—Tweed; (f) Hawick—Teviot; (g) Stirling—Forth.

10. The River Clyde in Glasgow has four passenger tunnels beneath it. Two of these tunnels carry the passengers by Underground railway.

1. Fair Isle jumpers and hosiery are of Moorish pattern, though Fair Isle is half way between the Orkney and Shetland Islands. The patterns are believed to have been taught to the islanders by the shipwrecked crew of *El Gran Grifon*, a vessel of the Spanish Armada wrecked on the Isle.

2. There are seven yards of tartan in a kilt.

3. If you said tweed got its name from the River Tweed you are wrong, though it is made along that river. Originally it was called twill and known in Scotland as 'tweel'. A London clerk misread the name, entered the cloth in his books as 'tweed' and it's been tweed ever since.

4. When a Clan's ordinary tartan was so brightly coloured that it would be too conspicuous when out hunting, a more sombre-coloured tartan was designed to tone with the moors and hills. A dress tartan is the normal Clan tartan on a white ground.

5. A philabeg is a kilt, so you would buckle it on round your waist.

6. One of the banking concerns in Scotland is the British Linen Bank, originally the British Linen Company, a textile firm.

7. There is a Kilmarnock bonnet, a Balmoral bonnet and a Glengarry bonnet, but each has a completely individual shape.

8. The Gordon Highlanders are the only regiment to wear black buttons on their spats. This is a sign of mourning for General Sir John Moore.

9. A weaving factory at Bridgeton, Glasgow specialised in making head-dresses for Arab sheikhs.

10.   Charles Macintosh (born 1766) was a Glasgow chemist. He invented the waterproof fabric, made of two thicknesses of rubber cemented together by naphtha, which is now used in making mackintoshes.

1. Both these castles are in Lanarkshire. Castle Dangerous is Douglas Castle, about nine miles from Lanark. Tillietudlem Castle is Craignethan Castle on the River Nethan, which runs into the Clyde at Crossford.

2. After World War Two the people of Scotland presented a flat in Culzean Castle, Ayrshire, to General Eisenhower for use during his life. When he was President of the U.S.A. and used it, Culzean became officially the White House during his residence there.

3. Castle Campbell, above Dollar, is known as Castle Gloom. It is a ruined stronghold of the Campbells. Doom Castle is the name given by Neil Munro, in *John Splendid*, to Dunderave Castle on Loch Fyne.

4. Queen Victoria bought the estate of Balmoral in 1852 and Balmoral Castle, inspired largely by Prince Albert, was built where a castle of the Farquharsons formerly stood.

5. The Stone of Destiny was kept in the Castle of Dunstaffnage, by Loch Linnhe, Argyll. It was later removed to Scone, and then Edward I took it to Westminster Abbey, where it has remained (except for one brief and remarkable period) ever since.

6. This is Duncan's description, in *Macbeth*, of Macbeth's Castle at Inverness.

7. Castle Moil, now a ruin near Kyleakin, was built by a Danish Princess, nicknamed by the Scots 'Saucy Mary'. She stretched a chain across the Kyle of Lochalsh, between the mainland and Skye, and took toll from every ship which passed through the strait.

8.   *(a)* Floors Castle is the seat of the Duke of Roxburghe; *(b)* Glamis Castle, the Earl of Strathmore; *(c)* Inveraray Castle, the Duke of Argyll.

9.   Edinburgh Castle esplanade was formerly used for executions. Now it is the parade ground where the Military Tattoo is an outstanding item of the Edinburgh International Festival.

10.   Queen Victoria so described Castle Grant, seat of the Countess of Seafield, near Grantown-on-Spey.

ANSWERS TO QUIZ NO. 25

1. A 'deoch an doruis' is the Gaelic for 'the drink at the door'.
It is a last drink to speed the parting guest.

2. Sugarolly water is made by mixing liquorice (chopped
small), sugar, and water in a bottle. It is usually kept beneath
the bed, the theory being that it will get blacker that way.

3. Atholl Brose is a drink made of heather honey, oatmeal,
and whisky.

4. A quaich is an old Scottish drinking vessel.

5. A Scots pint is about three pints imperial measure.

6. The Scots favoured claret because of the 'Auld Alliance'
with France. The English were allied to Portugal, so they
favoured port.

7. The most important single ingredient of whisky is the
water. The barley, grain, peat, and method of distilling all
affect the final product but it is the water that determines the
character of the whisky.

8. A hearty bumper of good drink is a 'richt guid willie
waucht'.

9. Bonnie Prince Charlie is said to have given the recipe for
the liqueur, Drambuie, to the MacKinnon Clan. It is still kept
secret.

10. The liquid shipped to London from Glasgow every night
is water. The Glasgow supply from Loch Katrine is the purest
in Britain, and London wine and spirit merchants have found
it the best liquid to 'reduce' rum, which is too strong to be
drunk in its original state.

[131]

1. The County of Bute in the Firth of Clyde is composed of the Isle of Bute, the Isle of Arran, and the Greater and Lesser Cumbraes. The counties of Orkney and Shetland are also all islands.

2. Fingal's Cave, one of the marvels of the world, is on the uninhabited Isle of Staffa, one mile long and about a quarter of a mile wide. The cave has a sixty-six-foot arch at the entrance and is 227 feet deep.

3. Duncan and Macbeth, and other Scottish Kings, are buried on the Isle of Iona. Christianity was brought to Scotland by St. Columba, who landed on Iona from Ireland.

4. Canna is noted for its Compass Hill, which, owing to the large proportion of iron in its basaltic rock, has the property of affecting ships' compasses.

5. The Outer Hebrides are said by the Gaels to have existed 'since before the Himalayas were beneath the seas'.

6. Neither the Black Isle nor the Isle of Whithorn is an island. Each is a peninsula.

7. The small rocky island annexed by Great Britain in 1955 is Rockall.

8. Ailsa Craig, the 1,000-foot rock in the Firth of Clyde, was held as a strong point on behalf of Philip of Spain when he planned his second attack on Britain.

9. The Isle of Eigg is the most musical island in Scotland because of its famous 'singing sands'.

10. The Bass Rock in the Firth of Forth was used as a prison for English captives and, after 1671, for Covenanters. Later four Jacobite officers were imprisoned on the Rock, but they disarmed their guards and held the Bass Rock against all comers for nearly three years.

1.   According to legend, there is a secret chamber in Glamis Castle, in which the Monster of Glamis is kept hidden. The secret of the monster is known only to the Earl of Strathmore, his heir apparent, and his factor.

2.   The Great Grey Man has been seen by a number of responsible mountaineers in the Lairig Ghru and at the top of Ben Macdhui. A University professor has recorded how he saw and heard the Great Grey Man, and other climbers have heard footsteps behind them, but only one for every two or three they took.

3.   A kelpie is a river spirit, and usually appears as a water horse.

4.   Sigurd, the Earl of Orkney, killed his enemy, Maelbrigd, cut off his head and hung it at his saddle bow. As he rode home, he punctured his leg on one of Maelbrigd's projecting teeth, and died soon afterwards from blood poisoning.

5.   Bocans and Bleaters are fairies found only on the Isle of Arran in the Firth of Clyde. Bocans are big, tough spirits who are dangerous to human beings. Bleaters are the Arran equivalent of Zombies. They drift into a house, sit by the fire, and weep all night.

6.   A banshee is a spirit whose wailing foretells death.

7.   The Trows are fairies of the Orkney and Shetland Islands and are the equivalent of the Norwegian Trolls. Edvard Grieg, in *Peer Gynt*, presented the Trolls. He was descended from a Scottish family named Greig.

8.   Granny Kempock is a standing stone on a hill behind Kempock Point at Gourock in the Firth of Clyde. In olden

days sailors walked seven times round Granny Kempock for luck and then took away some of the earth round the stone in a basket. This was supposed to prevent storms at sea. Three witches who plotted to throw Granny Kempock into the Firth were burned at the stake at Inverkip, a village near by.

9. The Bluidy Stair is part of the ruins of Rothesay Castle. The legend is that a Scottish Princess chose death rather than dishonour when the Vikings captured the castle, and her spirit is still seen on the stair where she killed herself.

10. Witches and evil spirits are most active on Hallowe'en, 31st October. That is the Eve of All Saints' Day.

1. As the population of Edinburgh increased between the sixteenth and eighteenth centuries, houses grew taller until they were the highest in Europe. Some were fourteen storeys high.

2. The biggest vine in the world grew at Kippen, but the area was sold to a housing project and the vine uprooted.

3. The cliffs of Foula are the loftiest and grandest in the British Isles. On this island they have a height of 1,220 feet.

4. The road to Applecross, Wester Ross, over Tornapress Hill, is the steepest in Britain. It rises 2,050 feet in five miles.

5. The Falls of Glomach, on the River Ault in Kintail, Ross-shire, are the highest in Britain, with a 300-foot sheer descent.

6. Gardner's furniture warehouse in Jamaica Street, Glasgow. It was later copied in the United States.

7. The highest main-line railway is that between Pitlochry and Inverness at Druimauchdar (popularly 'Drumochter') Pass, 1,484 feet.

8. The largest football stadium in Europe is Hampden Park, Glasgow. It made a world record for attendance at a football match when Scotland played England in 1937—149,547.

9. The first medical school in Britain was established at Aberdeen University in 1505.

10. The world's biggest passenger liners, the *Queen Mary* and the *Queen Elizabeth*, were built at John Brown's shipyard, Clydebank.

1. Dr. Johnson made this remark to a Scottish lady who immediately replied, 'And where will you see such horses and such men?'

2. E. V. Lucas described the Scottish National War Memorial at Edinburgh Castle in these terms.

3. (a) Lord Byron—'English Bards and Scotch Reviewers'; (b) Gerard Manley Hopkins—'Inversnaid'; (c) John Keats— 'Sonnet written upon the top of Ben Nevis'; (d) Wilfrid Wilson Gibson—'Flannan Isle'; (e) Thomas Babbington Macaulay—'Epitaph on a Jacobite'; (f) Robert Southey— 'The Inchcape Rock'; (g) Charles Wolfe—'The Burial of Sir John Moore after Corunna'; (h) William Wordsworth— 'Yarrow Revisited'.

4. This description of Glasgow was written in 1723 by Daniel Defoe.

5. And this description of Glasgow was the title of a pamphlet written by William Bolitho in 1924.

6. John Wesley, the evangelist, wrote this of Edinburgh in 1762.

7. The description is by Froissart, translated by Lord Berners. He is writing of the end of the thirteenth century and the beginning of the fourteenth.

8. This line is from *Macbeth* by William Shakespeare.

9. In an unsung verse of the national anthem the lines occur, 'Confound their politics, frustrate their knavish tricks.' This refers to the advance of Bonnie Prince Charlie's army against London in 1745.

10. This was said by Amyat, the King's physician, towards the end of the eighteenth century.

ANSWERS TO QUIZ NO. 30

1. St. Margaret, wife of Malcolm Canmore, King of Scotland.

2. St. Mungo, Patron Saint of Glasgow, is also known as St. Kentigern.

3. St. Ninian built the first stone church, the White House or Candida Casa, at Whithorn in the year 396.

4. St. Andrew is Patron Saint of Scotland, and his diagonal cross is used on the national flag. It is a white cross on a blue background. Russia once had St. Andrew as their Patron Saint, and their flag was a blue cross on a white background.

5. The senior football team of Paisley is called St. Mirren after the Patron Saint of the town.

6. St. Columba and St. Moluag raced for the island of Lismore. St. Moluag, afraid he was going to lose, cut off the little finger of his left hand and threw it ashore. Then he claimed to have landed first!

7. When a new bishop was appointed in Orkney, he had to drink from the cup of St. Magnus. The way and the amount he drank was supposed to indicate the manner and length of his tenure of the bishopric.

8. St. Columba built a monastery on the Isle of Iona in the year 563. It stood for 1,000 years, then fell into ruins.

9. St. Andrews owes its foundation to St. Regulus (or Rule), who landed there in the fourth century with some relics of St. Andrew.

10. The old name of Perth was St. Johnstoun, or John's town. St. John's is the parish church of Perth. The name is still kept alive by the city's senior football club, St. Johnstone.

1. (*a*) The Deil; (*b*) The Deil; (*c*) The Deil! These are all well-known Scottish names for the Devil.

2. The Devil's Mill is a waterfall on the River Devon, Kinross-shire. The Deil's Cauldron is also a waterfall, in a glen near Comrie.

3. The Deil is in the poems 'Address to the Deil' and 'Tam o' Shanter', and in the song 'The Deil's awa' wi' the Exciseman'.

4. Bridie brought the Deil into his first play, *The Sunlight Sonata*, made him the eponymous hero of *Mr. Bolfry*, and put him into his last play, *The Baikie Charivari* (seen at the 1959 Edinburgh Festival).

5. 'The Bad Fire' is a euphemism for Hell, used by Glasgow mothers who want to frighten their children into obedience: 'You'll go to the Bad Fire'.

6. The Devil's Beef-Tub, seven miles north of Moffat, is a steep-sided natural depression in the hills, used as a pound for animals stolen by the men of Annandale in the days of the Border cattle raids.

7. The Deil can play the bagpipes, according to Robert Burns. In 'Tam o' Shanter', Tam sees through the window of Alloway kirk:

> There sat Auld Nick in shape o' beast . . .
> He screwed the pipes and gart them skirl,
> Till roof and rafters a' did dirl.

8. The Devil's Elbow is a high pass with a very dangerous hairpin bend on the road running between the Cairnwell and Glas Maol, about ten miles south of Braemar. It is notorious for accidents.

9. The Devil's Point is a peak in the Highlands (in the Cairngorms). The Devil's Dyke is a low earthworks in the Lowlands—an ancient line of fortifications from Loch Ryan to the Solway Firth, believed to have been built about the time the Romans left Britain.

10. That means literally, 'The Devil take the last'. It's an encouragement to be up in front in whatever activity is on hand.

1. John MacLeod, an Army pipe major, heard a Sardinian band play the Ballet Music from Rossini's *William Tell* during the Crimean War. He adapted it for the pipes and called it 'The Green Hills of Tyrol'. It is one of the best known Retreat airs for pipe bands.

2. Felix Bartholdy Mendelssohn wrote *Fingal's Cave*.

3. 'The Road to the Isles' changes its title to 'The Burning Sands of Egypt' when it is played on the pipes.

4. The bagpipes were banned as a weapon of war by the British Government after the 1745 rising. Even today Army regulations allow a platoon in a Scottish regiment to have one man more than an English platoon. The extra man is the piper.

5. *(a)* Sir Alexander Gibson was the conductor of the Scottish National Orchestra; *(b)* Jimmy Shand is the father-figure of Scottish country dance music; *(c)* Iain Hamilton is one of the most modern of Scottish composers; *(d)* Rod Stewart is supreme in rock music.

6. Puirt-a-beul is Highland mouth music. When there are no pipers, fiddlers, or accordion players, the Gaels gather a small choir and sing the music for dancing.

7. 'The Scotch Symphony' is the name which Mendelssohn himself gave to his Third Symphony.

8. Pibroch is the classical form of bagpipe music, while Piob Mhor is the Great Highland Bagpipe itself.

9. A bugler of the Scots Guards sounded the 'Cease Fire' in Europe on 8th May 1945. Everyone who heard it agreed that it was the finest music in the world.

10. *Lucia di Lammermoor* by Donizetti is based on *The Bride of Lammermoor* by Sir Walter Scott.

1. The Thousand Pipers march at the Cowal Games held at Dunoon on the Firth of Clyde at the end of August.

2. There are twelve players in a shinty team.

3. The trunk of a tree, trimmed into a long pole, is tossed in the traditional event of Tossing the Caber.

4. The game of curling is played outside on ice in the Highlands, and inside on ice rinks in the Lowlands.

5. The Hop, Step and Leap, a traditional Highland Games event, is not an event at the Olympic Games.

6. Shinty is said by the Highlanders to be the fastest ball game in the world. The ball travels at great speed from one end of the field (larger than a football pitch) to the other, and spectators sometimes find themselves looking the wrong way!

7. Braemar Highland Gathering, which is customarily attended by members of the Royal Family, is held at the beginning of September.

8. To assist the curling stone to its target, curlers use brooms to sweep the ice free of any impediment. Two of them run just ahead of the stone, sweeping vigorously all the time.

9. At Aboyne Highland Gathering girl dancers must wear a bodice and skirt patterned on the old Highland style of dress.

10. No, you wouldn't. A caman is a shinty stick, and a bonspiel is a curling competition.

1. There are several carses, but only one Merse. The Carse of Gowrie is a typical carse—a stretch of alluvial fertile land alongside a river. The Merse (Marsh) is the largest plain in Scotland, just over the Border at Berwick.

2. The village of Comrie in Perthshire is situated on a geological fault, and is liable to slight earthquakes—so slight that it's seldom the inhabitants know they have taken place!

3. Duns is the county town of Berwickshire. Berwick, officially, is in England.

4. Lochnagar is an Aberdeenshire mountain; Lochaber is an Inverness-shire district; and Lochmaben is a Dumfriesshire town. Other 'lochs' with no water are Lochaline, a village; Lochcarron, village; Lochearnhead, village; Loch Fell, a mountain; Lochgair, village; Lochgelly, town; Lochgilphead, town; Lochgoilhead, village; Lochinver, port; Lochmaddy, village; Lochranza, village; Lochwinnoch, town.

5. Fingal's Grave is supposed to be at Killin, Perthshire.

6. Gold was once mined at Wanlockhead in Lanarkshire. Its height, 1,380 feet, makes it the highest village in Scotland.

7. Maidenkirk is Kirkmaiden in the Mull of Galloway. Johnny Groats is John o' Groats. The distance between them is 280 miles.

8. John o' Groats is *not* the most northerly point on the mainland of Scotland. It is Dunnet Head, not far away. The distance between Dunnet Head and Land's End is approximately 900 miles.

9. The Vikings, coming from Shetland and Orkney, called the country south of Caithness 'southern land'. It is now the

[143]

county of Sutherland and the most thinly populated in Britain, with fewer than eight persons to the square mile.

10. (a) Auch—field; (b) Ard—height; (c) Balloch—a pass; (d) Beg—little; (e) Buie—yellow; (f) Cam—crooked; (g) Clach—stone; (h) Dhu or Dubh—black; (i) Dun—fort; (j) Kil—cell or church; (k) Ochter or Auchter—upper, high-lying; (1) Craig—a rock.

1. The Pentland Firth, unlike the others mentioned, is open at both ends.

2. A Kyle is a strait.

3. The paddle steamer Waverley was built in Glasgow and still sails from there. She is as well known in England, Wales and Ireland as she is in Scotland.

4. There are only two Capes in Scotland—the well-known Cape Wrath, and Cape Difficulty in the Sound of Harris.

5. Among the islands in the Firth of Forth are May Island, Bass Rock, Inchkeith, Inchcolm, and Inchgarvie.

6. Inchgarvie, though the smallest of these five islands, is the most important because it supports the central pier of the Forth Bridge.

7. A bridge crosses the Atlantic Ocean between Argyll and Seil Island, and another between the islands of Bernera and Lewis.

8. The most northerly habitation in Britain is the Muckle Flugga Lighthouse.

9. Here are nine firths within the borders of Scotland—Beauly Firth, the Firth of Clyde, the Cromarty Firth, the Dornoch Firth, the Firth of Forth, the Firth of Lorne, the Moray Firth, the Pentland Firth, and the Firth of Tay.

10. In the Strait of Corrievreckan, between the islands of Jura and Scarba, is one of the world's most notorious whirlpools.

1. Before advancing into battle the Highlanders 'scrugged' their bonnets by soaking them in water, wringing them out, and pulling them down over their foreheads. The scrugged bonnets blunted a sword blow, and were almost as good as helmets.

2. General Monk raised the Coldstream Guards in the small Berwickshire town of Coldstream in 1650.

3. The only British subject allowed to keep a standing army is the Duke of Atholl. The Atholl Highlanders have their headquarters at Blair Castle, Blair Atholl.

4. The Cameronians (Scottish Rifles) take their rifles to church and post guards in memory of the original Cameronians, a Covenanting sect who, when they held a conventicle (or religious service), kept their arms beside them and posted sentries to watch for possible attacks.

5. The oldest Highland regiment is the Black Watch, founded in 1739. It got its name from the very dark tartan of the Black Watch kilt.

6. Third Lanark Football Club, Glasgow, was started by the men of the 3rd Lanarkshire Rifle Volunteers, now a Territorial battalion of the Cameronians. Until Third Lanark was disbanded, the players still wore the Cameronians' badge on their jerseys.

7. The Royal Scots are the senior infantry regiment of the British Army. They started as a Scottish contingent of mercenaries with King Gustavus Adolphus of Sweden. Then they became Hepburn's regiment, and finally the Royal Scots.

8. The Earl o' Mar's Greybreeks were the Royal Scots Fusiliers. The Glesca Keelies were the Highland Light Infantry. The two regiments were later amalgamated under the title of the Royal Highland Fusiliers.

[146]

9. The Royal Scots (see No. 7) are known as 'Pontius Pilate's Bodyguard'.

10. The motto of the Royal Scots Greys is 'Second to None'; that of the Argyll and Sutherland Highlanders is '*Sans Peur*' ('Without Fear'); and the motto of the Gordon Highlanders is 'Bydand', which means 'Waiting'.

ANSWERS TO QUIZ NO. 37

1. The Jacobites' treasure is supposed to be hidden some-where on or near the banks of Loch Arkaig in the Great Glen.

2. There are four different kinds of pound notes in current use in Scotland. They include those issued by the Bank of Scotland, the Royal Bank of Scotland, the Clydesdale Bank, and, of course, the Bank of England.

3. Gold was discovered in Sutherland, near Kildonan, in 1869 but in insufficient quantities to make mining profitable.

4. The air of the room where gold nibs are fitted to fountain-pens, in a factory at Leslie, Fife, is extracted every night so that the gold dust can be removed from it. This process saves hundreds of pounds a year.

5. The Duke of Argyll has made several attempts to locate the Spanish treasure ship which is supposed to lie at the bottom of Tobermory Bay, Isle of Mull. Objects have been brought up by divers indicating that there is a ship there, but it is not certain that it is the Spanish Armada ship which was carrying the sailors' pay.

6. The British Government offered a reward of £30,000 for the capture of Bonnie Prince Charlie in 1746. Though many Highlanders knew where the Prince was, during his five months in hiding, not one claimed the reward.

7. This is the old Scots coinage. Two doits equal one bodle; two bodles, one plack; forty placks, one merk. So you'd rather have a merk than any of the others.

8. Alexander Carnegie, the Scottish millionaire, was born in a cottage in Dunfermline. It is now preserved as a Carnegie

[148]

museum. The headquarters of the Carnegie Trust are in Dunfermline.

9. When William III needed money for the French War in 1694, he received a loan of £1,200,000 from Thomas Paterson, a Scot who had gone to London and become a merchant there. In return, the King allowed Paterson and his company to issue banknotes in London. That company is now the Bank of England.

10. The twelve lines were written by Burns on the back of a Bank of Scotland banknote dated 1st March 1780. They appear in collections of the poet's work under the title of 'Lines written on a Bank-note'.

1. On New Year's Day at Burghead on the Moray coast they light the Clavie (a tar barrel) and push it round the town until it disintegrates.

2. You must not say 'A guid New Year' until after the stroke of midnight on Hogmanay. It's considered unlucky to wish anyone a happy New Year until the New Year is 'in'. Scots people compromise by saying 'A guid New Year when it comes!'

3. During the Up-Helly-Aa celebrations in the last week of January at Lerwick, capital of the Shetland Isles, there is a great torchlight procession of men dressed as Vikings. They pull a full-sized Viking galley round the town and then, at a signal, they all throw their torches into the galley and set it alight.

4. On Hallowe'en, 31st October, children dress up as 'guisers' (in disguise) and go about the streets of some Scottish towns carrying lanterns made from turnips.

5. The 'Uppies' (people in the upper end of the town) play the 'Doonies' (people in the lower end) at handball all over Jedburgh on Candlemas Day, 2nd February. There is no limit to the number in each team.

6. The Burry Man appears at an annual ceremony in South Queensferry. He wears a special outfit, including a hood, covered with burrs.

7. (a) The Lanimer Queen is crowned on Lanimer Day (in June) at Lanark; (b) the Marymass Queen is crowned on Marymass Day (end of August) at Irvine; (c) the Queen of the South is crowned during the 'Guid Nychburris' festival (in July) at Dumfries.

8. A 'first foot' (first person to cross the threshold after midnight on Hogmanay) always takes gifts to the houses he visits. Those who can't afford anything better take a lump of coal. When they enter the house, they throw the coal on the fire and say, 'Lang may yer lum reek!'

9. A 'beardless bejant' (first-year student) plays the part of Kate Kennedy in an annual procession at St. Andrews University.

10. On a night in March the children of Lanark gather at the Town House with paper balls attached to strings. On a signal they chase each other round the building, trying to hit the child in front with the paper ball. It is said that 'Whuppity Scoorie' owes its origin to the scourging of a witch from the town.

1. To the tree in front of the Bailie Nicol Jarvie Hotel at Aberfoyle is fastened the coulter (poker) with which the Bailie, according to *Rob Roy*, defeated the Highland robbers.

2. Donald, Lord of the Isles in 1411, could claim that he had been at Oxford University.

3. Lord Clyde was born in Glasgow in 1792 and christened Colin McLiver. He joined the Army in 1808 as Colin Campbell, became Sir Colin Campbell, and finally Lord Clyde.

4. Dr. J. Y. Simpson experimented on himself with chloroform, which he discovered after experiments in Edinburgh.

5. John Paul, born at Arbigland on the Solway shore near Kirkbean, went to America and changed his name to John Paul Jones. He was the founder of the American Navy, and he was disliked in Scotland because he commanded American privateers which harried the coast. The dance 'Paul Jones' was named after him.

6. The Argyll and Sutherland Highlanders formed the 'Thin Red Line', and are the only infantry regiment to bear the battle honour 'Balaclava' on their colours.

7. Sir James Douglas (hero in Scotland and 'The Black Douglas' to the English) was taking Robert the Bruce's heart to the Holy Land when he was involved in a fight in Spain. He threw the casket containing the heart ahead of him and was killed charging into the fray after it.

8. Sir Alexander Leslie was Field Marshal of Sweden under King Gustavus Adolphus. He returned to Scotland to become commander of the Scottish Covenanting Army.

9. Two Clans, the Clan Chattan and the Clan Quhele, agreed to have a battle on the North Inch at Perth, an equal number of men to represent each Clan. When it was discovered that one Clan was a man short, a Perth blacksmith named Hal o' the Wynd, attached to neither Clan, volunteered to 'make up the side', just for the fun of it.

10. General Sir John Moore, who was buried at Corunna.

1. When Scottish nobles entered the Dominican Priory at Perth to murder James I, Catherine Douglas tried to bar the door by putting her arm through the staple. Her arm was broken, and the King was killed. As Rossetti wrote in *The King's Tragedy*:

> 'Twas Catherine Douglas sprang to the door,
> But I fell back Kate Barlass.

2. Mary Drummond went to London to help Mrs. Pankhurst in the suffragette campaign. Her planning was so good that she was known as 'General' Drummond.

3. Flora Macdonald protected Bonnie Prince Charlie after the rising of 1745. Some years later she emigrated with her husband and family to America. On the outbreak of the American War of Independence, she and her family supported the Loyalist forces, who were defeated.

4. Huntingtower Castle, near Methven, Perthshire, has two towers. Between them is the Maiden's Leap, so called because the Earl of Gowrie's daughter, afraid of being caught with her lover, jumped from one tower to the other.

5. The odd heroine out is Jeanie Deans, who is a fictional character in Sir Walter Scott's *Heart of Midlothian*. The others were real women.

6. Black Agnes was the Countess of Dunbar. The English besieged Dunbar Castle when her husband was away, but she conducted the defence for six weeks, until help came. When the English instruments of war scored a hit on the battlements, Black Agnes would dust the spot with her handkerchief to show her contempt for the enemy.

7. Mary Slessor, a Dundee woman, who went out to Africa as a missionary. She is sometimes known as Mary Slessor of Calabar.

8. There is a collection of suffragette relics on show in the People's Palace, Glasgow Green.

9. Agnes Murray of Ellibank, in the Border country, was the original of the legend of 'Muckle-mou'd Meg' (Big-mouthed Meg). She is the heroine of *Toom Byres* by Robert McLellan, and *The Warld's Wonder* by Alexander Reid.

10. The Countess of Buchan placed the crown on Robert the Bruce's head at his coronation in Glasgow. When she was captured by Edward I she was imprisoned in a cage which was hung on the wall of Berwick Castle.

ANSWERS TO QUIZ NO. 41

1.   There are 24 airports in Scotland. Some of them are air-fields and one is a cockle shore, but they are all served by regular flights.

2.   The Forth Bridge, of course. And when the painters are finished, they start all over again. The Forth Bridge is one mile, 972 yards long, and 450 feet high. It was built in 1883–90.

3.   The Vikings sailed their galleys up Loch Long to Arrochar. Then they dragged the galleys over the narrow pass between Arrochar and Tarbet, and relaunched them in Loch Lomond.

4.   It's very unlikely that the Scots mile will ever be run in four minutes, because it is 1,984 yards, compared with the normal 1,760.

5.   The first railway in Scotland was between Kilmarnock and Troon, Ayrshire, and was built in 1808.

6.   Loganair flight between Orkney Islands of Westray and Papa Westray. Scheduled for 2 minutes but in favourable wind conditions has been accomplished in 58 seconds.

7.   You would travel down 'Neptune's Staircase' by boat, since that is the name given to the series of locks at the Fort William end of the Caledonian Canal.

8.   No. The 'Shetland Bus' was the name used for the fishing boats which sailed between Shetland and Norway during World War Two and kept a link between the Norwegian underground movement and this country.

9.   The first Scottish passenger steamer was Henry Bell's Comet, which made regular voyages on the Firth of Clyde from 1812 to 1820.

speed that it can land in places impossible for a normal aircraft.

10. Only two of these trains are still running — The Flying Scotsman from Edinburgh and the Royal Scot from Glasgow.

1. The Electric Brae is on the road between Culzean Castle and Dunure. By an optical illusion you imagine that your car is climbing when, in actual fact, it is going downhill. This is tested by switching off the engine when the car still appears to be ascending.

2. The 37th Chief of the Clan is Baron MacLean of Duart and Morven. He is the Lord Chamberlain and in that office he supervised all the arrangements for the Royal Wedding.

3. Eyemouth on the Berwickshire coast was so famous as a smuggling centre that it was said there was as much below ground as above it.

4. The Trossachs, translated from the Gaelic, are 'the bristly country'.

5. Fortingall on Loch Tay is said to be the birthplace of Pontius Pilate.

6. This was written by Scottish University students about William McGonagall, Poet of Dundee. McGonagall's 'poems' are famous all over Scotland, have been the subject of many B.B.C. broadcasts, and appear in some nonsense verse anthologies. His own book of poems still sells well, and he is the hero of the play *Gog and Magog* by James Bridie.

7. King Arthur is supposed to have lived in the West of Scotland and now rests under Arthur's Seat, Edinburgh. King Cole, the merry old soul, was really King Coil, who gave his name to one of the districts of Ayrshire, where he lived.

8. In a cave on the Island of Davaar, off Campbeltown, is the Cave Picture of the Crucifixion, painted by Archibald Mackinnon, a Campbeltown artist, on the bare rock of the

cave wall. It was painted at the beginning of the century, retouched by the artist when he was eighty, and has been restored by the principal art teacher of Campbeltown Grammar School.

9. The equivalent of Gretna Green on the east coast of Scotland was Lamberton Toll, on the Scottish Border going north from Berwick.

10. The original house at John o' Groats was built in memory of Jan de Groot, a Dutchman who came to Scotland in the time of James IV. To prevent quarrels among his eight descendants, the house was built in an octagonal shape, with eight doors and an eight-sided table.

1. Alexander Mackenzie emigrated from Scotland to Canada at the age of sixteen and became a fur trader. His first expedition was down the river which now bears his name. His second was from Fort Chippewyan across the Rocky Mountains to the Pacific Ocean.

2. The interior of Africa was practically unknown until Mungo Park explored it. He tried to solve the mystery of the Niger, which some said was connected with the Nile, others with the Congo.

3. The saying (need I say it?) is 'Dr. Livingstone, I presume?' David Livingstone was a missionary, but an explorer too, and he discovered and named the Victoria Falls.

4. James Bruce discovered the source of the Blue Nile.

5. Donald Smith, Lord Strathcona, was instrumental in the building of the Canadian Pacific Railway.

6. The first white man to cross Australia from south to north was John McDowall Stuart.

7. Calgary in Canada was named by emigrants from the tiny village at Calgary Bay on the Isle of Mull.

8. Allan Pinkerton, who organized the secret service for the North in the American Civil War, came from the Gorbals, Glasgow. Later he founded Pinkerton's Detective Agency.

9. The province of Western Australia was founded by a Scot, James Stirling, and he named the state capital Perth after his friend and patron, Lord Perth. Brisbane in Queensland got its name from Sir Thomas Brisbane, a Scottish governor of New South Wales.

10. George Bogle, a Scotsman, led the first expedition from Warren Hastings in 1774 to make contact with the Grand Lama of Tibet.

1. Berwick changed hands thirteen times (did you notice the 'unlucky' clue?) before 1482. Although Berwick is in England, its county, Berwickshire, is in Scotland.

2. There are 72 MPs representing Scotland in the House of Commons.

3. The Five Sisters of Kintail are the hills enclosing Loch Shiel.

4. The Shetland Islands number 100, and twenty-four of them are inhabited.

5. The Seven Men of Moidart were the seven companions of Prince Charles Edward Stewart, who sailed with him to Scotland in *La Doutelle* in 1745.

6. 'The Glorious Twelfth' is the opening of the grouse-shooting season on the 12th of August.

7. There are six Lord Provosts in Scotland. Each of the following cities has one—Edinburgh, Glasgow, Dundee, Aberdeen, Perth, and Elgin.

8. There are four rivers in Scotland named Esk. The Dumfries River Esk flows south into England to the head of the Solway Firth. The Midlothian Esk flows to the Firth of Forth at Musselburgh. The county of Angus has two rivers —the North Esk flowing through Glen Esk to the North Sea north of Montrose, and the South Esk flowing from Glen Clova past Brechin into Montrose Basin.

9. The Three Sisters are mountains in Glencoe. They face the Black Rock across Loch Triochatan, where Ossian was

[161]

born. On one of them, Aonach Dubh, is Ossian's Cave, high up on the mountainside.

10.   An ancient stone circle at Holywood, near Dumfries, is known as the Twelve Apostles, but there are only eleven stones.

1. John Napier, born in 1550 at Merchiston Castle, Edinburgh, invented Napier's Bones, an early attempt at a calculating machine. He also invented a battle tank which was never used, and logarithms, which are used all the time.

2. John Logie Baird carried out electrical experiments with Jack Buchanan when they both lived in Helensburgh.

3. Kirkpatrick MacMillan, a Dumfriesshire blacksmith, invented the bicycle in 1839. When he first cycled round the countryside, amazed natives called him 'The Devil on Wheels'.

4. William Thomson, who took his title of Lord Kelvin from the River Kelvin in Glasgow, perfected the mariner's compass and pioneered the transatlantic telegraph cable.

5. James Watt got his idea for the steam engine when he was walking across Glasgow Green, and *not* when he was watching a kettle boil. At that time he was an instrument-maker at Glasgow University.

6. Alexander Graham Bell, of Charlotte Street, Edinburgh, invented the electromagnetic telephone in Boston in 1876. The first telephone, invented by a German schoolmaster, was not adopted, but Bell's was because it could transmit speech.

7. James Chalmers (1782–1853), a Dundee bookseller, is supposed to have first suggested adhesive stamps. Rowland Hill introduced the penny post in 1840.

8. William Murdoch (1754–1839), son of an Ayrshire millwright, went to England to seek his fortune and got his first job because his employer-to-be discovered that Murdoch had made his hat out of wood. In 1792 he lit his cottage at

Redruth, Cornwall, with coal-gas, and developed the use of gas as an illuminant.

9. John Loudon Macadam (1756–1836) was born in Ayr, emigrated to New York, and returned to become a road surveyor in England. He laid down a durable surface for roads, and we still talk of 'macadamized' roads today.

10. James Clerk Maxwell of Edinburgh discovered the wireless ray. R. A. Watson-Watt of Brechin was the great pioneer of radar.

ANSWERS TO QUIZ NO. 46

1. 'True blue' was a phrase first used by Covenanters. They decorated themselves with blue ribbons in opposition to the scarlet ribbon of Charles I, and the fashion was followed by the troops of Leslie and Montrose in 1639.

2. 'For auld lang syne' means 'for the time long since gone'. It should *not* be sung 'For old lang zyne'.

3. The Carron Company made a small gun which they named the carronade. The remedy for burns, Carron Oil, also comes from the name of the firm.

4. An 'auld wife's tale' nowadays means a story or a theory that has long been dropped as unreliable or out of date. Originally, it was a story of legend or history.

5. 'Jeddart justice' was practised in Jedburgh, where Border courts were held. The motto was, 'Hang first, and try him afterwards!'

6. A 'rider-out' in Scotland was a commercial traveller (or earlier, a packman) on horseback.

7. Yes, you would welcome a 'lad o' pairts' anywhere. He is a lad of parts, and that means he has qualities that should help him to rise in the world.

8. Whisky has been called 'John Barleycorn' since Robert Burns used that name in one of his poems about the wine of the country.

9. You would play bridge, whist, or any other card game with 'The Devil's Books', for that is the Scottish Presbyterian name for a pack of cards.

10. A 'lang pedigree' should be applied to people. Scottish lairds and ladies were very proud of their 'lang pedigree', and would take their listeners through it at the slightest excuse.

[165]

1. The Auld Alliance is regarded as starting about 1295, when John Baliol was on the throne of Scotland and sought France's help against Edward I of England.

2. In the days when anything approaching modern sanitation was more or less unknown in Edinburgh, housewives and servants in the Old Town would simply throw the contents of slop pails out of the window. As they did so, they shouted 'Gardy-loo!', which was a corruption of '*Gardez-l'eau!*' or 'Beware of the water!'

3. Haggis is supposed to be the Scottish version of a French dish known as *hachis*.

4. The Scottish version of gauche is gawky (awkward); of gentil, genteel (polite); and of bien, it is bien or bein (well-doing or comfortable).

5. The first Scots Guards were '*la garde Ecossaise*' of the Kings of France, formed under the Auld Alliance, and regularized by Charles VII in the fifteenth century. It consisted of 100 men-at-arms and 200 archers, of whom twenty-four were 'special protectors of the royal person', and six were the King's close bodyguard on ceremonial occasions.

6. Shortbread was brought by the French to Scotland.

7. Dour is from the French *dur*, meaning hard, and douce is the same word in French, meaning sweet, but used in Scotland more as quiet and sedate.

8. She would mean 'Bring the dishes out of the cupboard'. The Scots word ashet comes from the French *assiette*, a plate. Aumrie comes from the French *armoire*, a cupboard.

9. Little France is a small village on the outskirts of Edinburgh where once lived French servants brought from France to Scotland by Mary Queen of Scots.

10. A Scotswoman would ask for a gigot of mutton. Gigot is a term used by Scottish butchers and unknown among their English counterparts.

1. The biggest shipbreaking concern in Scotland is at Faslane on the Gareloch, Firth of Clyde.

2. (a) Silk—Dunfermline; (b) lace—Darvel and Newmilns; (c) tweed—Harris; (d) knitwear—Hawick; (e) linoleum—Kirkcaldy; (f) jute—Dundee.

3. Singer's Sewing Machine Factory at Clydebank (now reconstructed as an industrial estate) had the biggest clock in the world.

4. The Thames-Embankment is made of granite from the great quarry at Kemnay, near Aberdeen.

5. When David Dale opened his mills at New Lanark he provided an 'improver' for each of his workers. This was a small block of wood, hung at the side of the loom. Each side was painted a different colour and, according to the side showing, it could be seen whether the operator was working well or not. White meant 'excellent', yellow was 'good', blue was 'room for improvement', and black was 'bad'.

6. Gourock Ropeworks in Port Glasgow made the ropes for many ships, including the *Cutty Sark* and the *Queen Elizabeth*, and also big tops for the circus.

7. Arran Chiefs and Arran Banners are two of the varieties of potato bred by Donald McKelvie on the Isle of Arran. Seed potatoes of these varieties go all over the world.

8. Scotland's biggest export industry is whisky.

9. The distilling of whisky is unique because, by law, Scotch whisky can be made nowhere else in the world but

[168]

Scotland. Foreign whiskies are usually identifiable by the spelling 'whiskey'.

10.   All are sites for power stations. Dounreay and Hunterston—nuclear power. Loch Sloy—hydroelectric power.

1. The four oldest Scottish Universities are: St. Andrews, 1411; Glasgow, 1451; Aberdeen, 1494; Edinburgh, 1582.

2. Robert and Andrew Foulis opened an Academy of Fine Arts in Glasgow University Library in 1755. They were also famous as printers.

3. Sir James Murray edited *The Oxford English Dictionary*, accepted as the standard authority on English words.

4. Glasgow High School pupils who became Prime Ministers were Sir Henry Campbell-Bannerman and Bonar Law. The Hutcheson's Grammar School pupil who became Governor-General of Canada was John Buchan, Lord Tweedsmuir.

5. Joseph Lister began antiseptic surgery in Glasgow Royal Infirmary. Sir Ronald Ross discovered that the mosquito was the carrier of malaria. Sir Alexander Fleming discovered penicillin.

6. He was a Scot named James Crichton, who distinguished himself in his teens as a brilliant scholar and linguist. He was killed in Italy in 1582 at the age of twenty-one.

7. James Rennie designed the old Southwark, the old Waterloo and London bridges. Thomas Telford designed the Menai and Conway bridges in Wales.

8. Alexander Cruden wrote the standard Bible concordance.

9. Samuel Smiles, who wrote *Self Help*, was born in Haddington, East Lothian.

10. McGill University, Toronto, was founded by James McGill from Glasgow.

[170]

1. Devorgilla, wife of John de Baliol, and mother of the Scottish King known as 'Toom Tabard', was joint founder with her husband of Balliol College, Oxford. In 1275 she founded New Abbey and ordered that, when she died, the heart of her husband was to be placed in her tomb. Thereafter it was known as Sweetheart Abbey.

2. Bonnie Prince Charlie (I was determined he would be in at the death!) pretended to be Flora Macdonald's Irish maid, Betty Burke, to get through the English lines from Benbecula to Skye on 29th June 1746.

3. The Prentice Pillar is in Rosslyn Chapel, near Edinburgh. An apprentice carved it in the absence abroad of his master. When the master returned, he was so jealous that he slew the apprentice with a mallet.

4. The 'Burns of the North' was a Gaelic poet named Robert Donn, who could neither read nor write. He is buried at Durness, Sutherland.

5. It was alleged that, when the infants were taken off Inchkeith and brought to Edinburgh, they had evolved a 'very guid Ebrew' (Hebrew) tongue.

6. They are both churches. The 'Lantern of the North' is Elgin Cathedral, now a ruin. The 'Lamp of the Lothian' is the Abbey church of St. Mary in Haddington,

7. Berwick on the Scottish Border is technically in England, but Berwick Rangers are in the Scottish League and play in the Scottish Cup.

8. There is no need to avoid the Edinburgh Ell. It is one of the ancient Scottish standards of measurement.

9. Moscow is a small village to the north-east of Kilmarnock. Rome is a group of a few houses to the south-west of Kilmarnock.

10. No, you wouldn't like to join 'The Merry Dancers'. That is a Scottish name for the Aurora Borealis.